Praise for *Please*

"This is the story of the Alma Mater (Nourishing Mother) of the movement to stop doctors worldwide from committing atrocities, which harm their patients for life."

—**George C. Denniston**, MD, MPH, co-editor of NOCIRC's eight books of presentations from the International Symposia on Genital Autonomy and Children's Rights, co-editor of *Say No to Circumcision!: 40 Compelling Reasons,* and the founder of Doctors Opposing Circumcision.

"Marilyn Milos's *Please Don't Cut the Baby! A Nurse's Memoir* is a timely book, appearing as it does amid growing bioethical and human rights concerns over non-therapeutic infant male circumcision and genital mutilation in general. Knowing, as we do today, that children, even before birth, are sentient, conscious, and remembering beings, the trauma inflicted upon them by such surgical interventions represents a life-long wounding on their bodies and psyches that will adversely affect them. Prevention trumps treatment. Future parents need to read this fine book."

—**Thomas R Verny**, MD, DPsych, DHL (Hon), FRCP(C), FAPA, Author of *The Secret Life of the Unborn Child, The Embodied Mind*

"In 1980, Ed Wallerstein dedicated his book, *Circumcision: An American Health Fallacy,* to 'healthcare providers who have already disavowed the necessity of routine newborn circumcision.' After advocating against medically unnecessary circumcision for decades, Marilyn Milos epitomizes the enlightened healthcare providers my father's book was dedicated to. Had he lived to see the publication of *Please Don't Cut The Baby! A Nurse's Memoir,* my father would have whole-heartedly endorsed Marilyn's new book."

—**Les Wallerstein**, JD, M.Psych

"Male and female circumcision is a crime, and to be more precise, it is the greatest crime committed by humanity against its weakest members. Knowing Marilyn Milos and her courage and persistence in tackling this crime, I would like to encourage everyone to read her book *Please Don't Cut the Baby! A Nurse's Memoir.* I hope it will soon be translated into all languages so that this crime finally stops."

—**Sami Aldeeb Abu-Sahlieh**, Doctor of Law, Centre de Droit Arabe et Musulman, author of many books, including *Male & Female Circumcision Among Jews, Christians and Muslims: Religious Medical, Social, and Legal Debate*

"When Marilyn Milos recruited me to join a team of doctors fighting infant circumcision at a conference in San Francisco in 1996, I had no idea what I was getting into. She helped reshape my career in wellness through activism. Over a quarter of a century later, as I delight in her long awaited memoir, I marvel at her abilities to inspire generations of men and women to take up the cause of genital justice. It's my fervent hope that it will inspire future generations to complete this work, even if they never are as lucky as I am to experience this force of nature firsthand."

—**John Travis**, MD., MPH, Alliance for Transforming the Lives of Children (aTLC)

"Routine infant circumcision is both an unnatural and unnecessary surgery, as males have been living with their foreskins for many centuries with no adverse effects. Marilyn Milos devoted her life to saving male babies from the trauma and pain of circumcision, leaving an important legacy to carry on for humanity—preserving the integrity of the foreskin."

—**Daniel J. Gillet,** French Intactivist

"The first dictum of ethical medical practice is 'Primum Non Nocere' (First Do No Harm). In contrast, much of the medical profession in the United States and other English-speaking countries has deliberately and knowingly violated this fundamental tenet of ethical medical conduct, by subjecting defenseless children to cruel and harmful circumcisions that can result in traumatic, lifelong psycho-sexual harm. This book about the *tragedy of infant male circumcision* illustrates the author's enormous courage, and that of other ethicists throughout the world, in tackling head-on this useless and harmful non-therapeutic sexual reduction surgery imposed on many non-consenting and defenseless minors, including normal, healthy baby boys."

—**Gregory J. Boyle**, PhD, DSc, FAPS

"This book is a wonderful, comprehensive history of the high points of the birth and maturation of the intactivist movement in the U.S., told in Marilyn Milos's clear, brave, empathetic voice. But interwoven is also a satisfying deep dive into the background that prepared Milos to take on her leadership role: she stood up to an abusive parent. Her work with Lenny Bruce and Ralph Ginzberg gave her the tools to talk freely about sex and genitals; and she trained and worked as a nurse. As a participant in much of this history myself, I couldn't put the book down. It was riveting."

—**Tina Kimmel,** PhD, MSW, MPH

"Many nurses don't realize the power they have to effect change, much less use it. Marilyn Milos has shown us the way to freedom from our archaic role as handmaids to torture and abuse. When the nurses at my hospital took a conscientious objector stand to stop assisting with newborn circumcision, Marilyn empowered us with love, support, and counsel. She is a role model for our profession. And who knew she could play the banjo!"

—**Mary Conant**, RN, co-founder,
Nurses for the Rights of the Child

"Marilyn is an indefatigable force of nature whose path led her to protect the most vulnerable among us. Her story shows what one person can accomplish with sheer determination and strength of will. The take-home lesson is change occurs with each personal encounter. Talk to people, don't be discouraged, and never give up."

—**Robert Van Howe**, MD, MS, Provisional Medical Director,
The Western Upper Peninsula Health Department (WUPHD)

PLEASE DON'T CUT THE BABY!

a nurse's memoir

MARILYN FAYRE MILOS

with Judy Kirkwood

LUCID HOUSE PUBLISHING

Published in Marietta, Georgia, United States of America by Lucid House Publishing, LLC
www.LucidHousePublishing.com

This title is available in print and e-book via Lucid House Publishing, LLC as well as an audiobook in partnership with Blackstone Publishing.
Cover and interior design: The Design Lab Atlanta, Inc
Author photo: Kevin Garrett

This memoir is based on the author's memories along with her decades of experiences as the mother of the anti-circumcision movement. She has devoted most of her life to this cause and has conducted extensive research into the topic. This book also contains portions of emails and communications from different people, whose lives have been touched in some way by the practice of male genital cutting. Several names have been changed for the sake of privacy.

Library of Congress Cataloging-in-Publication Data:
Milos, Marilyn Fayre 1940-
Kirkwood, Judy 1950-
Please don't cut the baby: a nurse's memoir/by Marilyn Fayre Milos and Judy Kirkwood–1st ed.
Library of Congress Control Number: 2023950543
Print ISBN: 978-1950495498
E-book ISBN: 978-1950495535
1. Biography 2. Family dysfunction 3. Civil Rights Activist 4. Circumcision
5. Child sexual abuse 6. Genital mutilation 7. Children's rights 8. Medical ethics
9. Grateful Dead 10. NOCIRC 11. Intact America 12. Nursing
BIO032000
BIO019000
FAM035000
Lucid House Publishing books are available for special promotions and bulk purchase discounts. For details, contact info@LucidHousePublishing.com

This book is dedicated to:

~

every baby and child, each of whom deserves and
needs our love, respect, and protection;

~

parents who know it is their responsibility to protect
and defend their baby's rights, and to those parents
who are willing to learn;

~

and healthcare professionals who honor the normal body,
support children's rights, and tell parents the
truth about circumcision.

Contents

Not the End

FOREWORD

By Dean Edell, MD
Mendocino County, California

True pioneers are an unusual lot. They decide to give their lives to a cause and follow through. Many of us dream about changing our world in some way but few ever get even close. Marilyn Milos is one of those unique people who pulled it off.

The devotion and passion she brought to her life's work made it quite an experience to be around her. A furious tornado of energy swirled about her at all times. And, as the fastest talking human on earth, she never ran out of words. Marilyn's commitment to her cause was a force to be reckoned with.

What was the subject of this ferocity? A small piece of human tissue at the tip of a baby's penis—the foreskin—or more accurately, the lack of it after routine circumcision.

It's a wonder to me that it took so long for circumcision to rise in the public conversation about healthcare and human rights. There was a palpable void. Perhaps a subject that dealt with the human penis was bound to be verboten in polite conversation, as well as on the federally regulated airwaves. Maybe it took a female to push the truth about circumcision onto the national stage because men themselves were not at all well informed about this routine travesty that affected them not only as infants but for their entire lives.

In 1983, when I first got involved in Marilyn's crusade to inform the public, as well as healthcare professionals, about how circumcision is not medically necessary, most men barely knew what circumcision was—even though most American men were circumcised. Until they were confronted by an uncircumcised penis in a locker room or in any foreign country other than Israel or Islamic nations, they might as well have arrived on the planet stripped of their foreskin. Simply put, in the conservative Reagan years during which Marilyn created NOCIRC, National Organization of Circumcision Information Research Centers, most Americans did not know what an intact penis looked like.

I met Marilyn when she and her colleague, Sheila Curran, came to the KGO studio because I'd invited them to show me their video on circumcision, *Informed Consent.* Marilyn then helped in putting together a two-part mini-documentary that aired for two nights on the medical segment during the evening news. I saw Marilyn again in the hospital just after my fourth son was born. Marilyn was educating mothers on the obstetrical ward about circumcision and telling them the American Academy of Pediatrics did not recommend it. That didn't sit well with hospital brass, and Marilyn was fired shortly afterwards—a fortunate event because that gave Marilyn the time and incentive to launch her protest movement.

While Marilyn's inspiration for educating the country on circumcision was the emotionally searing experience of witnessing a screaming baby tied down and forced to have a surgical removal of critical penile tissue, I came at it with a scientific public health and journalistic interest. My radio and television careers were taking off and Marilyn regaled me with a barrage of information that just clicked in my brain. Here was something no one was talking about in the national media. It was a no-brainer for me, and a story made for media—sex, religion, human rights, genitals, and babies. It had legs, as media pros would put it. We did lots of stories on radio and television and print media together.

A quick perusal of the medical literature on the subject revealed a gaping intellectual hole. Back in the nineteenth century, John Harvey Kellogg, in his copious cornucopia of health advice, advocated circumcision to prevent masturbation and sexual impropriety. So strong was his belief that he circumcised himself at age 37! The primary excuse in the later twentieth century for nonreligious circumcision was that we would prevent future medical problems of the penis by surgically removing part of it from a newborn infant. Using the same logic, shouldn't we be removing infantile breast tissue from female infants to prevent breast cancer? Maybe while we're there, grab other troublemakers like a gallbladder or an ovary? The prevention of disease was an outmoded myth, and the foreskin turned out to have important functions instead of being useless excess tissue.

In short, there was no logical or medical reason to routinely circumcise all baby boys born in the U.S. Other countries had mostly abandoned this practice long ago. As parents started informing themselves, they easily saw the ruse and made appropriate decisions. Marilyn was indefatigable in her efforts to bring this to the public's attention. As Marilyn pushed and her organization NOCIRC grew, she brought her message to an ever-widening audience around the world. Marilyn organized annual international symposia, produced a variety of publications, and coordinated street protests at medical conventions and the offices of major medical organizations. She put this issue on the map.

The subject had so many different angles that more stories began to appear in print and electronic media. Mainstream medical organizations like the American Academy of Pediatrics started weighing in and more publicity was generated. Even though they sometimes were too wishy-washy on the subject, I trusted that as more people were aware of the controversy, they would make the right decisions. We managed to stir up a hornet's nest among diverse groups, from angry rabbis and pediatricians to adult women who had never seen a foreskin in person.

When female circumcision started making headlines, the hypocrisy of male circumcision was exposed. The pro-circumcision community pushed back with blind defensiveness. There was the thorny question of religious freedom and the right to perform blood rituals. American pediatricians and obstetricians initially were unconvinced until many looked at the research, saw no evidence to justify this gross violation of a baby's body, and joined the movement. Objective research papers on sexual function and feelings are far and few between. Marilyn designed and implemented a scientific controlled study published in the *British Journal of Urology* that proved the circumcised penis was much less sensitive than the intact penis. Men who were circumcised as adults came forward and reported their experiences. The momentum was building and circumcision rates in the U.S. started to fall. But not far enough.

Marilyn has said many times that she won't quit until the practice completely disappears from the American medical landscape. I believe her. Yet, in her ninth decade, it may be time for her to sit down for a minute and catch her breath while others carry the banners and spread the word.

Marilyn's personal story, which you will read here, reveals furious devotion and an unwillingness to give up against overwhelming odds.

For those who believe that one person cannot change the world, you are wrong. Yes, of course, Marilyn had cohorts and helpers along the way without whom her success would have been muted. But educating America about circumcision started with one nurse who was outraged by one extremely common medical procedure others thought was routine and appropriate. I might have been one of those "others" if not for meeting Marilyn.

I was born Jewish and participated in the ritual of circumcision with my first three sons. After meeting Marilyn, it was impossible to acquiesce to medically unnecessary circumcision for my fourth son. He is pushing 40 now and intact, and so is his son. Thanks, Marilyn.

PREFACE

When I decided to write a book about the history of NOCIRC and the movement to stop routine infant circumcision, for which I have been both blamed and credited, I showed an early draft to several friends. They each asked why I hadn't included myself in the book. I explained that this book isn't about me: it is about the babies. They insisted that, if not for me, we wouldn't be having this discussion, and the book would be more interesting if I included myself.

To be honest, I have often wondered why no one else was ever as moved as I was to end nontherapeutic circumcision of infants and children. I became an advocate for parents to make an informed decision about circumcision from the moment I first witnessed a tiny infant's reaction to this misguided ritual. Having incorporated material about the things in my life that shaped me, I now understand how my earlier years were preparation for my work.

As I stepped onto this path, I worried about how I would fund myself and the advocacy I was intending, hoping, and wanting to do. At every roadblock, fork in the road, incident of road rage—and there were many attempts to derail me on this path—I found encouragement from different sources. Someone sent me the following quote attributed to Mother Teresa:

God is Love in action, and

He can move you any time

to serve a need.

If He shows you a need

to be served, He will provide the resources.

So you can trust totally—And, don't you organize too much.

Goethe reportedly said the same thing a little differently:

The moment one definitely commits oneself, then providence moves too. All sorts of things occur to help one that would never otherwise have occurred. A whole stream of events issues from the decision, raising in one's favor all manner of unforeseen incidents and meetings and material assistance which no man could have dreamed would have come his way. Whatever you can do or dream, you can begin it. Boldness has genius, power, and magic in it. Begin it now!

Thankfully, these quotes have proven true for me.

I began working on this book in 2018, but the isolation of the 2020 pandemic finally gave me the opportunity to settle into the work it takes to write a book—something for which, along with book *editors,* I have a new respect. Now in my eighties and knowing that the women in my family died during this decade of their lives, I have a sense of urgency to complete this project as part of my life's mission.

This book offers both a beginning and an end, as I pass the torch to others to carry on informing the world about the issues that surround the very important decision of whether to circumcise a child. To be clear, unless there is a legitimate medical reason for circumcision, I believe—based on everything I have learned in more than four decades of study and exchange of information with both experts in relevant fields and feedback from countless humans who have experienced circumcision—that it is our responsibility to end the routine mutilation of those who do not yet have a voice to say "No!"

FINDING MY VOICE: THE MAKING OF AN ACTIVIST 1975–1979

Chapter 1

AWAKENING

I filed into the newborn nursery with my fellow nursing classmates where we saw a newborn baby strapped spread-eagle to a plastic board. I was immediately disturbed by what I was seeing and hearing. Before me was a precious baby struggling against his restraints—tugging, whimpering, and crying helplessly.

This was May of 1979. I was a nursing student completing my last rotation on the obstetrical unit at Marin General Hospital in northern California before my graduation from the College of Marin.

At the age of 39, I did not know what circumcision was, although I had three circumcised sons by then and was no stranger to birth or to newborn babies. As a lay midwife, I had assisted with the homebirth of many babies before I enrolled in nursing school. But I don't remember anyone debating the pros and cons of circumcision immediately before or after birthing. I certainly was not prepared for the reality of circumcision or what I would learn later was the needless suffering of a fragile newborn baby.

Since no one was tending to this new little being, I asked my instructor if I could comfort him. She replied with, "Wait til the doctor gets here." I wondered how a teacher of the healing arts could watch a baby suffer and not offer assistance.

When the doctor did arrive, I immediately asked him if I could help calm the baby. He told me to put my finger into the baby's mouth. I did and the baby began to suck. I stroked his little head and spoke softly to him. The baby began to relax and was momentarily quiet.

The silence was soon broken by a piercing scream—the baby's reaction to having his foreskin pinched and crushed as the doctor attached a hemostat (a metal clamp with interlocking teeth) to his penis. His shriek intensified when the doctor inserted another hemostat between the foreskin and glans (head of the penis), tearing the two structures apart. The baby started shaking his head back and forth—the only part of his body free to move—as the doctor used another clamp to crush the foreskin lengthwise, which he then cut. This made the opening of the foreskin large enough to insert a device that protects the glans from being amputated during the surgery.

The baby began to gasp and choke, breathless from his shrill, continuous screams. How much longer could this go on?

During the next stage of the surgery, the doctor crushed the foreskin against the protective device that covered the glans and then finally amputated it. The baby was limp, exhausted, spent.

Nothing could have prepared me for seeing a part of this baby's penis being cut off—and without an anesthetic. As I watched the baby suffer and scream uncontrollably, my chin began to quiver, and I couldn't keep myself from bursting into tears. The doctor looked into my eyes and said, ***"There is no medical reason for doing this."*** I couldn't believe my ears. My knees started to buckle, and I felt sick to my stomach.

How could a doctor, dedicated to helping and healing, inflict such pain and anguish on a healthy newborn baby with no medical justification? Yet when the doctor looked directly into my eyes, I knew he understood my agony, and he may even have shared it. After all, he had admitted there was no reason to cause such trauma to a newborn.

In an instant, my focus shifted. What had I, in my training to be a nurse, participated in? What had I allowed to be done to my own sons? In my defense, I didn't know what circumcision was when my husband consented to the circumcision of our sons. My doctor told us the surgery was a necessary health measure, didn't hurt, and only took a minute—like cutting the umbilical cord, I thought. I now know that was not true. My doctor had lied to me.

I went back to the classroom with the rest of the nursing students, who also thought what had happened was horrible. I did not yet know I would devote the rest of my life to challenging the basis for circumcision. And I would not know for some time the backlash that occurs when change challenges personal preference, cultural conditioning, medical mythology, religious affiliation, the dominant paradigm, the status quo, the current medical model, and financial incentive.

Having been awakened to the unnecessary trauma of circumcision, would I simply be a witness to something I knew deep in my soul was a travesty and injustice to a tiny baby delivered into our care and protection? Impossible. I *had* to do something about it! This was my life-changing moment.

Chapter 2

MARRIAGE, MOTHERHOOD, AND THE WORD "CIRCUMCISED"

In the summer of 1957, I was 17 and my fiancé Joe was 19. "I need to tell you something," Joe said in a serious tone. *"I'm not circumcised."*

I had never heard that word before. I had no idea what Joe was talking about, but was too embarrassed to say so, too shy to ask, and couldn't remember the word to look it up. I just knew he didn't feel good about himself, so I said, "Don't worry, honey. I love you just the way you are."

Joe had graduated from Palo Alto High School, and I had graduated from Menlo-Atherton High School, both in the Bay Area. A mutual friend introduced us. Joe planned on attending San Jose State that September. I was working at Stanford Research Institute as a stenographer. We were each still living with our parents.

One night I got home ten minutes after my father thought I should have. I explained that Joe had to work a little late that evening. My father wouldn't listen to reason and he hit me. It was not the first time. He slugged me with his fist, slammed me into the wall, and continued to hit me until I peed on the floor. He left the room and never mentioned the incident again. In fact, he never apologized for any of his abusive behavior.

After this particularly violent encounter, Joe decided to rescue me from my volatile home life. We were married at my parents' home by a local minister on January 30, 1958, two months before my 18th birthday. Both families attended our small wedding.

I got pregnant just two months after we were married, proving diaphragms are not always trustworthy. At a doctor appointment about a month before our baby's due date, the doctor asked Joe and me, "If your baby is a boy, do you want him *circumcised?*" There was that word again. I still didn't know what it meant. I turned to Joe, who looked at me and started to say something, but the doctor interrupted him and said, "It doesn't hurt, only takes a minute, and will protect your son throughout life." I heard the word *protect,* which obviously made me think circumcision was good for a baby. It never occurred to me to ask for details or that my doctor would lie about something so painful, traumatic, and unnecessary.

Joe turned to the doctor and said, "Yes."

In retrospect, I think Joe, who was born in 1938, may have been teased when he was in school or in the Marine Corps Reserves, which he had joined upon graduation from high school. Perhaps he didn't want his son to suffer the same teasing, ridicule, or embarrassment that he had for being different.

I told Joe's mother what the doctor had said to us about circumcision. She said that when Joe and Jim, his identical twin brother, were born, her doctor told her that *not all babies need to be circumcised*—which was why Joe and his brother were not. Although her comment led me to believe that this circumcision thing was negotiable, I trusted my doctor would know and do what was right for our baby. I had no reason not to.

Our beautiful baby, Michael, was born on Christmas Day, 1958.

In those days, when a woman entered the hospital in labor, she was on an assembly line. Her pubic hair was shaved, she was given an enema, and an IV was inserted into her arm. She was left alone to labor, with no support, then strapped down on her back for the birth with an oxygen mask placed over her nose and mouth. Her perineum was routinely cut to widen the vaginal opening for birth and then sewn up after the baby was born. The baby was taken away immediately and brought back to her every four hours for feedings (even though newborn babies need to nurse more often than that). Moms were encouraged to bottle feed—and to circumcise their sons. Some of these disturbing practices are still prevalent in hospitals today.

Michael was circumcised the day we left the hospital. He was just four days old. Not knowing otherwise, I thought the clamp on my baby's umbilicus and the clamp on his penis were comparable. I didn't notice that my son's penis was different from his father's intact penis. I had never seen Michael's little body whole because he was whisked away immediately after he was born. I didn't see him again until the next morning. New mothers weren't allowed to undress their babies or change their diapers while they were convalescing in the hospital.

How could I have submitted to those absurd rules that ran so counter to my natural maternal instincts and my inherent rights as my baby's mother? Because I believed that the nurses and doctors knew best, as I had been programmed to believe. And I was very young.

Joe and I went on to have another beautiful son, Troy, in 1961.We weren't even asked about circumcision for him. The doctor just did it. I was still uninformed and ignorant. When we brought our sons home, we never discussed circumcision or the Plastibell circumcision device our babies had on their penises, which fell off when the tied-off remnant of their foreskins died and fell off, too.

It would be 20 years before I realized the truth about circumcision, its causes, and consequences. I wasn't uninformed by choice. I was uninformed due to a cultural fraud perpetrated by the medical establishment in the United States about circumcision.

Our daughter Kate was born in 1963. When I was just four months pregnant with her, Joe committed himself to Agnews State Mental Hospital (originally known as "The Great Asylum for the Insane") in the middle of the night. He called me the next morning to tell me where he was. Since I had been distraught throughout the night when he didn't come home from work, I was reassured to hear Joe was alive and okay. But what was this about?

I was not aware that Joe was in such mental or emotional distress, so this came as a complete surprise. Joe worked the late shift, and I wondered what could have caused him to do such a drastic thing after work. He had not spoken to me about his plans. Being self-committed, he was required to spend three months at the hospital, so I moved with my two young sons back into my mother-in-law's house, where we had lived after we first got married.

My mother-in-law was nurturing and supportive of me and the boys and was just as confused about what was going on with her son as I was. Joe's twin Jim was living in the house with his wife and two sons, too. Jim's wife Pat was pregnant with her second son when I was pregnant with Michael. Her son Bob was born on Christmas Eve and

Michael was born just hours later, on Christmas Day. Our sons have been close throughout their lives.

The house in South Palo Alto was not far from the Stanford University campus. Joe and Jim had helped their father build the three-bedroom, two-bath house, which had a large living room. It was a comfortable space for us all and I felt lucky to be welcomed there.

While Joe was in the hospital, I drove back and forth to visit him. I took the books he requested, his banjo, and music albums. He played music on a radio show he was hosting at the hospital. He told me about dances he attended and a young woman to whom he was attracted. He seemed to be enjoying himself there, whereas I was worn out with my pregnancy, chasing two small children, visiting Joe, and meeting his requests for the things he wanted at the hospital.

Years later, Joe told me he had committed himself to get out of the military after his request for conscientious objector status was denied. I was relieved to know, at least, that I wasn't the reason. I had been blaming myself since the night he hadn't come home. I don't know why he didn't share that information with me at the time, as it would have explained something that didn't make sense at all and had caused me so much guilt and grief.

When Joe finally did leave the hospital, I knew things had changed. He wouldn't talk to me about what was going on with him. He was cold and distant and couldn't look me in the eye. Then, just five weeks before Kate was born, Joe left me a note (at his mother's house) telling me he was leaving me. It was a remarkable note, especially the part that said, "Any attempts to contact me will be *thwarted.*"

"Thwarted?" What an interesting word to use in an "I'm dumping you" letter from the man who was the father of my sons and our soon-to-be-born daughter. To say I was shattered would be an understatement.

I spoke with the psychotherapist who treated Joe at the mental hospital. The doctor suggested I focus on myself and my children and reminded me to be thankful for them. Since I already was doing those things, his comments were not helpful. My children's father had abandoned me and our children. My world was falling apart. Was this the best the therapist could offer? I was overcome with grief, sorrow, and shame. How was I going to care for two young boys and a new baby by myself? I didn't even have a car. How could I work to support us? I was 23 years old.

As if this wasn't enough to deal with, I couldn't keep living with Joe's mother. Although she had been welcoming at first, she told me she wanted to sell the house and gave me two months to move out. Years later, she gave the house, which she had not yet sold, to Jim and his wife, and they all lived in the house together until they each died during the years that followed. I did understand that she, too, was in a difficult situation.

Despite Joe's request that I not "thwart" his wishes, I wanted Joe to experience the birth of our daughter. With our sons, the doctor had said he would do what he could to have Joe in the delivery room. But when the time came for those births, Joe wasn't allowed in. The doctor apologized, saying he had tried but it just wasn't possible. His response to my request for this birth was the same and I knew Joe wouldn't be permitted in, despite the doctor saying he would try.

Early in my pregnancy with Kate, I met Tina and David Meltzer, who lived in San Francisco. Tina was an artist, David a poet, and together they made beautiful music. David's impressive account, "Journal of the

Birth," about the homebirth of Tina and David's first daughter, Jennifer Love, appeared in *The Journal for the Protection of All Beings,* a City Lights publication. David's reaction to the birth was so wonderful and luminous that I thought that if Joe was able to witness the birth of our baby girl, his heart would open, and perhaps he would want to come home to me and our children.

Tina gave me the contact information for Dr. John Miller. Although he was no longer doing homebirths or having fathers in the delivery room (not yet a common practice or allowed by most hospitals), Dr. Miller promised Joe would be with me for the birth of Kate. "How can you do that if it's not allowed?" I asked. He said, "If they won't allow Joe into the delivery room, we just won't make it to the delivery room."

With confidence, I called my previous doctor to tell him I had found an obstetrician who would allow Joe in the delivery room to see the birth of his third child and that I would no longer be his patient. To my surprise, the doctor blurted out, "The delivery room is no place for a father!" It was apparent that he had *never* intended to allow Joe into the delivery room, no matter what he said. He had lied, plain and simple. My belief about the goodness of doctors and my ability to trust them was eroding bit by bit.

I did not want pain medication with my first two babies. But once I crossed the hospital's threshold, I lost my options. I was on a conveyor belt to a medicalized, technologically programmed, fear-based hospital birth. Business as usual. My wishes were ignored.

After the birth of my second son, and especially after meeting Tina, I realized that the birth I wanted to have was possible, but not at Stanford Hospital, nor with a doctor who had learned to "deliver" babies in medical school and had no idea how very beautiful the normal birth process could be. Neither storks nor doctors "deliver" babies. *Women* birth their own babies. Dr. Miller knew this, honored the process, and kept his promise. Joe was with me at French Hospital in San Francisco to witness the birth of our daughter during my first natural childbirth. Dr. Miller trusted women's bodies and did not interfere with the birth process. Joe and I both wept at the miracle of Kate's birth.

I was ecstatic. But even though Joe was deeply moved by the birth of his daughter, he never came back to live with us. We divorced a few years later when Joe's girlfriend got pregnant.

Five years later, when his second marriage was falling apart, Joe wrote to me saying, "Leaving you was my first mistake." I felt sad and sorry for him, knowing he would live with that mistake for the rest of his life. But by that time, I was in a new and magical relationship with the man who would be the father of my third son. Joe died from esophageal cancer in 2002.

Chapter 3

GROWING UP AND LIVING IN A CHANGING WORLD

Although our marriage didn't last, I will always be grateful to Joe for opening my eyes and my heart to injustice, and for valuing the importance of speaking up when something needed changing. As the world around us was gaining a social conscience, my personal world was also completely transformed during the years (1958–1963) that we were together.

Because I grew up in a home where compassion and meaningful communication were in short supply, I don't remember ever feeling valued before my life with Joe. My childhood was notable mainly for waiting for time to pass. My mother would send me outside to play but the street on my block was empty. With no other children around, I would often sit on the curb until I was called in for dinner.

Like the scene in *Wizard of Oz* where Dorothy's life changes from black and white Kansas to Technicolor Oz, after meeting Joe, my mind began expanding at a rapid rate. I became aware of a rainbow of vibrant colors that had been absent from my life. By the time the cultural changes of the sixties arrived—civil rights, the free speech and anti-war movements, feminism, the social and sexual revolutions—I was ready.

Growing up in San Mateo County, California, in the 1950s in an upwardly mobile middle-class family, life was largely wall-to-wall beige.

Menlo Park might have had a bit more chrome, but the point of life was conformity. My father, a steel salesman, thankfully was rarely home. I had a younger brother, Courtland, but we were not close as children. He was my mother's favorite because he was an easier child. My energy and curiosity were not traits that were rewarded by my domineering, abusive father, who spanked me when I was a child, and smacked or punched me when I was older. My mother often reminded me that I wouldn't get so many beatings from my father if I would just learn to keep my mouth shut. Maybe that's why my speech is noticeably faster than that of most people, or so I'm told. I needed to get out what had to be said before I was punished and sent to my room. I'm still trying to get out what I need to say before someone tries to shut me up.

From an early age, I was aware that my father was a racist. The summer I was nine years old, he took our family to Colorado Springs where he had grown up. I remember him pointing to a Black man—the first I had ever seen, which gives you an idea of the diversity of my life in San Bruno and East Palo Alto, the towns in which I spent my first ten years. He said, "See that man over there? He's black because he works in the coal mines."

I burst into tears because I knew my father was lying and that what he was saying was unkind. I saw a man whose skin was a different color, which I knew was that color when he was born, not from working in a coal mine. Why would my father say such a thing to me? What was his point? I didn't know what racism was, but I knew lying was wrong.

I'm grateful that my mother treated all people equally. When I was ten years old, my parents moved to Menlo Park because three Black families had moved into East Palo Alto and my father worried about the value of our house going down. I was sad because I liked the new children in the neighborhood.

My parents never discussed politics, world or national news, literature, or art. My mother read romance novels and my father read shoot-'em-up Westerns. In our home, how we looked was more important than developing our minds. I was a smart kid, my mind always racing, and I longed to be listened to, heard, and have my questions answered.

I was skipped from fourth to fifth grade in the middle of the year after testing high on an IQ test given to me at school. I was hungry for knowledge, but not for information as presented in the *Encyclopedia Britannica, Jr.* that my father had bought for me. School didn't stimulate my mind or alleviate my boredom. I got okay grades but, after missing the content of a year of school, I had no idea what I was doing in school or why. I was lost until my sophomore year biology class, which was the first inkling I had that there was structure in the world in which I lived. After that I became an honor student, taking anatomy as a junior and physiology as a senior.

Even though I was in a suburban white-bread bubble at age 16, somehow, I became aware of Allen Ginsberg's iconic poem *Howl*, published in 1956 in San Francisco, a mere 30 miles away—although it might as well have been a thousand miles. I knew there was a bigger world in which I belonged, where I would not feel isolated or be punished for my hunger for truth.

I had wanted to go to Mills College, a private liberal arts women's school in Oakland, California. My father wanted me to go to San Jose State. I went there to visit but was overwhelmed by the large campus and I didn't like the stern, unfriendly woman who ran the boarding house in which I would live.

I didn't have to decide about going on to school after my father beat me up that last time. Instead, my path led to being with Joe, marriage, and motherhood. I didn't go back to school for another 18 years.

As for my father, he was smart at his work and did his part to financially support us, but by the time he died in 1966 at age 55 of lung cancer, he had gambled away just about everything he had. I felt sad for him, but not loss. My mother found a job renting apartments and she would have one to live in, too. She kept that job until shortly before she died. By that time, I was a busy wife and mother with my own children to care for. Over the years, I have come to realize that my father did the best he could considering his own early life and the years in which he lived. That has made it easier to forgive him.

Once I was no longer living under my father's reign of fear, I was exposed to new and different perspectives on life and history. Joe was learning to play the banjo during that time. We listened to Southern Appalachian Mountain music, bluegrass, and folk music. I heard songs about coal miners who crawled six miles a day on their hands and knees to provide people with heat, warmth, and energy and their own families with food, while breaking their backs and destroying their lungs in the process. I heard songs about enslaved people in the South who worked on cotton plantations under the hot sun and in poor conditions. I knew about enslaved people, of course, but had never felt or fully realized the heartbreak and injustice of their lives, deprived not only of freedom but of basic human dignity. We were listening to the precursors of 1960s protest music, including Pete and Mike Seeger, Woody and Arlo Guthrie.

Kepler's Bookstore in Menlo Park was a destination for progressive thinkers at that time. Jerry Garcia was hanging out there and playing his guitar. I had known Jerry since he and my brother were in fourth grade together. He spent lots of time at our house, especially when he and Court were working on a class play together. Jerry also was an artist, and he drew the background for their play on a large sheet of butcher paper taped to a wooden frame that was placed as a backdrop on the stage. At the end of their play, Jerry exited by walking "through" the door he had drawn on the backdrop. The audience roared. Court said, "He stole the show!" Jerry was a performer even at about age nine.

Joe had been taking banjo lessons from J.P. Pickens and had gotten pretty good, so one day in 1961, I took him to Kepler's to meet Jerry. After introductions and conversation, Joe began playing his banjo as Jerry played guitar. They sounded great. For the next year or so, Jerry and mandolin and banjo player Ken Frankel came to our house on Sundays to practice. Joe also played the gut bucket (a washtub, broom handle, and bass string contraption). They called themselves the Thunder Mountain Tub Thumpers. They would practice then sit around the dinner table eating whatever I cooked, talking about music, and promoting their new band.

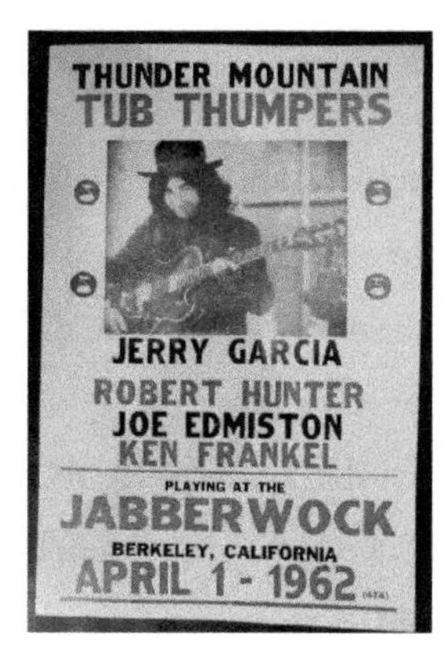

Photo of poster belonging to Marilyn Milos

Joe had taught Jerry how to play the banjo and, after Joe left me, Jerry came to my home every week to give me banjo lessons. I continued to take lessons from Jerry after I moved from South Palo Alto to Burlingame, closer to my parents' home so my mom could help me with the children. I began teaching beginning banjo lessons one night a week at a local music store, but it didn't last long because my students rapidly surpassed my abilities. I could teach the basics of playing the banjo but, as much as I love music, I am not a musician. Still, I'm grateful to have been taught to play banjo by Jerry, who two years later became the heart of the iconic rock band, the Grateful Dead.

In 1963, Tina and David Meltzer, with whom I had become friends when I was pregnant with Kate, were playing music at the Coffee Gallery on Grant Avenue in San Francisco. Hugh Romney, later known as Wavy Gravy—an entertainer, peace activist, and unofficial mascot of the Grateful Dead—was doing stand-up comedy at the Coffee Gallery, too. He asked Tina if she knew anyone who could type and take shorthand. Tina, knowing I could type, gave my name and phone number to Hugh. He, in turn, gave my contact information to an American stand-up comedian and social critic who integrated satire, politics, religion, and sex in an open, free-style form of comedy. His name was Lenny Bruce.

All I knew about Lenny prior to meeting him came from a short article I had read in the *San Francisco Chronicle*. It said something about a comedian being arrested for obscenity. I wondered what was considered obscene but didn't think much more about it at the time. Lenny needed a secretary while he was working in San Francisco, and I needed a job. I was still living in Burlingame and was receiving money from Aid to Families with Dependent Children because Joe was not paying child support.

Lenny and I met for the first time at the Swiss American Hotel on Broadway and Columbus Avenues in San Francisco's North Beach. He was performing at a club called Off Broadway. He asked me to take dictation and type a letter to Dorothy Kilgallen, a media personality, author, journalist, and television-show panelist on *What's My Line,* popular in the 1950s and early 1960s. Lenny was tried and found not guilty for obscenity in San Francisco, but now was facing trials in both Chicago and New York. Kilgallen, whom Lenny had never met, took it upon herself to come forward and stand up for him in the New York courtroom, as did many other notables.

Lenny had been arrested during a New York performance. A court reporter had transcribed a tape recording of his show for the trial. In the courtroom, witnesses were asked to read that transcript and determine if Lenny was guilty of obscenity. However, no one could understand the transcript, which contained more than 2,300 errors and consequently was incoherent. On the witness stand, Kilgallen told the judge and jury that Lenny was not obscene, but instead was a brilliant social critic who used the language of the people when performing. The letter I typed for Lenny thanked Dorothy Kilgallen for her kind support.

During the time I worked for Lenny, I transcribed dozens of recordings of his shows, including the tape of his Chicago show, where he also was found not guilty, and that New York show for which he was arrested. My transcriptions were accurate, but Lenny asked me to take dictation in longhand because, although I was a fast typist, I wasn't good at reading my own shorthand.

At one point during the New York trial, Lenny said this to the judge (paraphrased from memory):

> Your Honor, peace officers were sent to attend my show and take notes. When asked about my show, the officers reported how many times I said words *they* determined to be "obscene." That's all they got out of my show, and now I'm having to defend *their* interpretation of *my* work.

> When I say, "I am pissed off, Your Honor" it doesn't mean I'm urinating off the roof of a building; it means I'm "irritated" or "angry." Meanings of words change with time.
>
> District Attorney Richard Kuh responded by saying, "That's *poppycock*!"
>
> Lenny picked up his dictionary and read aloud to the judge the original meaning of the word "poppycock," which is "soft feces" or "dung."

The District Attorney had proven Lenny's point. After spending day and night working on his defense, after having been found not guilty for obscenity in San Francisco and Chicago while doing the same performances, Lenny had become an expert on obscenity laws. Still the New York court found Lenny guilty of obscenity.

After the guilty verdict, Lenny's performance at Carnegie Hall, where he had previously played to a packed house, was cancelled. Club owners across the country hired Lenny, only to be visited by Alcohol and Beverage Control agents, a fire marshal, or someone from one licensing board or another who put pressure on club owners to cancel the show.

Lenny's last performance was on June 25, 1966, at the Fillmore Auditorium in San Francisco. He stayed with my children and me in our North Beach apartment, where we'd moved after my father died. Lenny's depression was apparent as he talked about being found guilty. He could not return to the state where he had grown up. He was broke and unable to work. The pressure put upon club owners who wanted to hire him was unassailable.

That weekend Lenny spoke with the owner of Basin Street West. He had worked there for a couple of years after Off Broadway closed. He had been paid $4,000 a week for his shows there. Now the owner was offering him $400 a week. Lenny felt both demeaned and devastated by the offer. It was probably the final straw. I felt sorry for this caring man who worked so diligently to both entertain and educate the public about social injustice.

Lenny took his own life two months later in his home in Los Angeles. The media sensationalized his death as a drug overdose rather than the suicide of a brilliant social critic driven to despair by small-minded people with enough power to torment and silence him. Why do we kill the visionaries, the messengers, the ones willing to tell the emperor he is naked? This is a question I would come to ponder every day, as I took up the cause of protecting baby boys from brutal and needless surgery.

Working with Lenny taught me how power can create injustice and obscenity within the legal system. He used to say, "In the Hall of Justice, the only place you find justice is in the halls." Lenny's gift was his ability to explain inhumanity with humor, with the hope that humor would open hearts and allow people to hear the message.

In 2003, 37 years after his death, Lenny received a posthumous pardon from then-Governor George Pataki, the first posthumous pardon in New York State history. Lenny finally got the justice he deserved.

● ● ●

Six months after Lenny died, my North Beach friends Jeannie, whose children went to the same pre-school as my children, and her husband Bob, a house painter, invited me to dinner and an evening in North Beach to play pool and listen to music. Bob's assistant, Matt

Milos, was also invited. The spark that Jeannie and Bob hoped would be ignited between the two of us lit up.

It was spring 1967 in San Francisco. As the Summer of Love was beginning to blossom, so did a romance between Matt and me. It truly was a summer of love—a magical time with extraordinary music every weekend in the Panhandle or Golden Gate Park. Jerry Garcia and the Grateful Dead, Jefferson Airplane, Big Brother and the Holding Company, and Country Joe and the Fish were just some of the groups making names for themselves. Chuck Berry, Janis Joplin, and many other notables played at the Fillmore, Winterland Ballroom, and other venues in the city. My relationship with Matt deepened in the magic of it all.

Much has been made of the drug scene in San Francisco at that time. But the Summer of Love represented so much more than drugs. It promoted the ideals of communal living, sharing, and community ties while rejecting materialistic values that had tended to isolate people in the ticky-tacky boxes of their homes. The Free Store, the San Francisco Free Medical Clinic, and the Hip Job Co-Op all served those in the community. More than anything, the Summer of Love promoted political and cultural awareness and compassion for others, which resulted in a feeling of unity of humankind—and, yes, LOVE.

The Days of Rage that so exemplified the late sixties and early seventies were yet to come: the assassination of Martin Luther King, Jr. in April 1968, which led to rioting and racial tensions; the assassination of Senator Robert F. Kennedy in June 1968, which contributed to political turbulence and civil unrest; and, the icing on that cake, the Democratic National Convention in Chicago in August where unrestrained police violence met the resistance of antiwar demonstrators.

I would learn as much from demonstrating in the streets and taking direct action as a political strategy as I did from listening to music with Joe and Jerry Garcia and talking with friends about all the issues on our minds in the late sixties. I was in a place, San Francisco, surrounded by freethinkers, around whom it was safe to speak my mind and discuss issues that weighed on my heart. My voice was to become the tool for my vocation.

Chapter 4

EARLY ACTIVISM

Matt was not only my partner and husband during our years together but also a father to Michael, Troy, and Kate since Joe was not in their lives. Our newly formed family moved from North Beach to a larger apartment in the Haight-Ashbury district, across the street from Golden Gate Park. The Park was a wonderful playground for the children and a great place for music every weekend. With three school-age kids, my focus was on educating them in a way that didn't involve comparisons or grades but acknowledged individual interests and healthy ways of absorbing information.

Part of the 1960s counterculture movement was reimagining what education could and should be: education reform. I had been working with other parents and educators to create an alternative school we called Shire School. We had read *Summerhill: A Radical Approach to Child Rearing* by A.S. Neill (published in the U.S. in 1960), about a school founded in the 1920s in England where children participated in the structure of their education, not only choosing what they learned but also self-governing by peer, rather than adult, rule.

We held classes during the summer of 1967 in our homes until we located a building. Shire School opened in September 1967,with 60 teachers (most were part-time, coming in to provide specific classes in their fields of expertise) and 132 students, one of the largest alternative schools at that time. We created a space and curriculum where children could choose what they wanted to learn and have fun while at school rather than sitting in a chair at a desk all day.

Unfortunately, the school was shut down after only two months when the fire marshal and building inspectors declared the building we had rented unsafe because it wasn't earthquake proof. It is still standing today, five decades later, unscathed by the various seismic events since then.

To us, this showed how alternative education threatened the status quo and the powers that be. We were determined, however, that our children would not be indoctrinated into conformity. We moved our classes to the Panhandle, a park that is basically an extension of Golden Gate Park bordered by Fell and Oak Streets.

We would drive up to the lovely children's park, take our tables, chairs, books, and other supplies out of our cars and begin our school day. Teachers like biologist and Master Gardener Nan Koehler would come and take the children for walks, talking with them about plant and animal life everywhere. I loved going on these walks with her and the kids. When it became cold and rainy, we were invited by several churches to hold our classes inside.

When Nan became pregnant, I told her about Dr. John Miller, his trust in the birth process and mothers' bodies, and his willingness to let dads into the delivery room. She, too, had a beautiful birthing experience with Dr. Miller. When she gave birth to her second son, she was living in another state and decided to deliver the baby herself. After that experience, she became a lay midwife—something that interested me very much and that I tucked away to think about later.

Founding Shire School and participating in communal education was a wonderful experience that prepared me for grassroots organizing and creative ways to challenge the oppression of institutional ideas that were rooted in policy and assumptions rather than evidence.

● ● ●

When school let out, our family drove to the East Coast so Matt could spend time in Troy, New York, with his father, who was dying of cancer. At the same time, my friend Helen Haight Stoll was moving to New York because her husband, Jerry, was opening a documentary film company there. Jerry had just finished a documentary, *Sons & Daughters* (music by Jon Hendricks with Jerry Garcia and the Grateful Dead), explaining to parents why their children were marching in the streets against the Vietnam War. Matt, the children, and I had joined others in San Francisco for several demonstrations against the war. We also had gone to the San Francisco premiere of Jerry's documentary.

With Matt and Jerry otherwise occupied, Helen and I rented an unfurnished house a block from the beach in Winthrop, Massachusetts, for the summer. We moved in with her four children and my three, furnishing the house with sleeping bags, two borrowed card tables, and our suitcases. We sat on the suitcases around the card tables for our meals. Improvising was never a privation for us; it was an adventure.

The kids who lived nearby came to see the activity at the house and meet their new neighbors. They thought we were strange, living with no furniture. Plus, our five boys all had long hair when we arrived. As the summer went on, peer pressure and the need to be accepted meant shorter and shorter hair.

Matt and Jerry would come to visit us on weekends when they could get away. Our kids were making friends. With the beach just a half block from our house, we were all enjoying the sand, surf, and one another. The folks who lived next door ignored us. But they had a puppy. So, when Helen cooked meat (I'm a vegetarian), I'd save the scraps and bones for the puppy as a way to get to know our neighbors, who also had a new baby. I began to exchange baby stories with the mama, which broke the ice.

Our neighbors became more comfortable with us, which made for a more congenial atmosphere, considering we spent so much time outdoors. They seemed to enjoy talking to Helen, a gentle, quiet woman, more than to me. But that was no surprise. Once I had found my voice, I used it! I knew I could seem outspoken, opinionated, and maybe a little too inquisitive. But I loved getting to know people, exchanging stories and experiences, learning and teaching at the same time.

Louie, the husband, was a plumber, anti-hippy, and according to his assistant, Bill, also a racist. I got along well with Bill, who began coming over to visit us after work. Bill asked us not to tell Louie that he was Jewish, which we promised. It was mindboggling to us how one person could accept another person based on their skills and personality, yet reject that same person if they thought they belonged to a particular religion, race, or ethnic group they disliked. Louie had not gotten the message that we were all guests on the same planet, or, as Ram Dass said, "We're all just walking each other home."

One evening, when Helen and I were visiting Louie, his wife, and Bill, Louie got to talking about Black people. As I was biting my tongue to keep from revealing everything I was thinking, Helen, in her calm, sweet voice said, "Well, Louie, I think white men are prejudiced against

Black men because they're insecure about the size of their own penis and their own sexuality." I thought Louie was going to explode! He stood up, pointed to the door, and told Helen to get out. Of course, I left with her. It took several weeks of providing bones for the dog and being especially nice before Louie spoke to us again.

One weekend when Jerry came up from Manhattan, he and Helen took care of all the kids so Matt could take me to Troy, New York, to meet his father. His father still smoked despite having throat cancer. I was shocked to see this dying man put a finger over the tracheotomy opening in his neck to inhale cigarette smoke, and then a moment later take his finger off the opening to let the smoke escape from his neck.

Matt's grandparents were hoarders, and I could see that his father John (Matt's mother had died years earlier), in turn, never got rid of anything after they died. There was only a tiny path from the front door to the kitchen. Furniture consisted of a table and a single chair. From that chair, John could reach the sink, the stove, the refrigerator, and the television set. From his chair and the table, there were two more paths—one to the bathroom, the other to his bedroom. Stacks of boxes lined the little paths in the house, holding, among other essentials, rolls and rolls of toilet paper, yellowed with age. I remember feeling acutely sad for whatever Matt's family had experienced that caused such fear, need, and greed. I never saw John again. We returned after he died to empty the house and prepare it for sale.

Matt came and stayed with the children and me while Helen went to Manhattan to visit Jerry one weekend. On another weekend, Matt took the children and me to Provincetown, where he had worked as an apprentice for a man who made elegant picture frames. Our first night there, after the children had gone to sleep, Matt and I listened to the sound of gentle rain falling on the metal roof of the cabin. That night our son Timothy was conceived.

With summer ending, we drove back to San Francisco. We had given up our place in the Haight-Ashbury district when we left for the East Coast. Our friend Jeannie, who had introduced us, said we could stay with her family in North Beach until we found our own place.

Our landing back in San Francisco got rocky fast. Matt told me he would stay some nights in Berkeley in his frame shop in the Phoenix Gallery on College Avenue. It wasn't long before I realized Matt was having an affair. I learned who the woman was and called her home one afternoon. Matt answered and when he realized it was me, he blurted out, "No one is here."

I simply said, "It doesn't matter who is there, Matt. What matters is that you're not being honest with me." I hung up. Matt rushed back to San Francisco, and we began some very long talks that lasted for weeks. In the meantime, the other woman ended her relationship with Matt. A nice outcome of that difficult time is that she and I are still friends.

A sweet apartment near Jeannie's place in North Beach became available and I rented it.

Matt helped me move and settled back in with the children and me.

Our son Timothy was born in March 1969. When the doctor asked if we wanted him circumcised, Matt said, "Yes. I think a circumcised penis looks better." That concept had never even occurred to me because I still didn't know what the word meant or the difference between intact and circumcised penises. I did wonder, though, why my one-day old baby slept for eight hours after we brought him home from the hospital. By then, I knew newborns normally sleep two hours, and often less, between feedings.

It was another 10 years before I realized that Timothy slept so long because he was recovering from the trauma he'd suffered when his foreskin was amputated without pain relief.

When Timothy was two, Matt's father died. The sale of his house gave Matt and me enough money for a down payment on a home for our family. We moved across the Golden Gate Bridge to Woodacre, in the San Geronimo Valley in Marin County.

Once the children were enrolled in school, I began talking with Kate's teacher, Sandy Dorward, about Shire School and the possibility of setting up an alternative classroom within the public school system. Sandy also had read Neill's *Summerhill* and appreciated his philosophy about teaching. We began talking to other parents about an alternative classroom and many agreed that it was a wonderful idea. The Open Classroom was launched in 1971, when Kate was in second grade.

The Open Classroom allowed children to move from one subject area within the classroom to another, space permitting, as their interest was sparked. We held group meetings every morning with students, teachers, and the parents who were volunteering for the day. Following our meeting, every child worked in their notebook at their own pace, with the help of teachers, parents, and other students. They were learning to read, write, do research, and make change—the necessary things in life—while enjoying the freedom of the Open Classroom. They also had a garden and chickens to care for, and a wonderful playground designed and built by school board representative and father Richard Sloan, his helpers, parents, and the kids. Everything was done by group effort, and everyone was a part of the group.

I taught classes from the day the Open Classroom began until Timothy (five years younger than Kate) had gone through the program. I offered vegetarian cooking classes and hiked with the kids and another parent, Aneice Taylor, to map trails for the San Geronimo Valley Planning Commission. I began to take anatomy and physiology classes at the College of Marin, so I taught those subjects to the kids, too.

I also tutored anatomy students at the College for my professor and assisted with a College for Kids science class that Timothy attended when he was nine or ten. Later, he said it was that class that inspired him to become a scientist and then an outstanding winemaker and consultant in the Napa Valley. He was only a tot when he began accompanying me to the Open Classroom so, in a way, he had been absorbing its content and values from the age of two.

I am delighted to report that the Open Classroom, a program in the Lagunitas School, is still going strong today, 50 years later. Our *Summerhill*-inspired, parent/teacher child-centered alternative to mainstream education in the U.S. was proof, both then and now, of a quote attributed to the great cultural anthropologist Margaret Mead: "Never doubt that a small group of thoughtful committed individuals can change the world. In fact, it's the only thing that ever has."

I had found my voice as part of the counterculture's revolution of values in the 1960s. The establishment of Shire School, and then the Open Classroom, further empowered me to trust my instincts. I was gaining experience in productive grassroots organizing. And I had demonstrated my skills to myself and others as a teacher. Sharing what I learned came naturally to me. It was exciting, and it was a joy.

Chapter 5

THE SEVENTIES

While I was teaching in the Open Classroom during 1971, Matt's younger brother, John, came for a visit. He was planning a trip to Afghanistan and wanted to send some hashish to Matt. I told him not to send anything to our post office box. I said that if he wanted to take that risk, he should send it to his own PO box and pick it up when he returned. I did not want an illegal substance from halfway around the world turning up in our mail!

But that is not what happened. First, John sent a postcard from Afghanistan with a photo of a man in a loincloth sitting on a beautiful rug, with various hookahs and other paraphernalia around him. John wrote on the card that, although marijuana was difficult to purchase there, hashish was plentiful. I was livid. I had told John not to send anything, but it looked like that wasn't going to stop him; not to mention he had tipped off everyone in the post office that a potential drug delivery was in the works since his postcard message was clearly visible to anyone between Afghanistan and our little post office in Woodacre who had an opportunity to read it.

Two weeks later, as Christmas neared, I picked up several packages from the post office and took them home. That's when I saw the package from Afghanistan—and realized that it had been opened. I gave it to Matt and said, "Look what your brother sent us! What are you going to do about it?"

Matt took the package out to the aviary and put it under the chicken coop, saying, "No one will stoop down in chicken shit to look for it. I'll call our lawyer tomorrow, and we'll turn it in."

As I was cooking dinner, I heard a loud knock on the door. When I opened it, I was pushed backward into the house as five or six police officers rushed in. Meanwhile, Matt had gone into the bathroom to flush a marijuana joint down the toilet. A policeman ran into the bathroom and came out with a smirk on his face and a soggy, toilet-water-soaked joint draped over his first finger.

The cop handcuffed Matt's wrists behind his back and sat him down on a kitchen chair. Timothy, who was two at the time, jumped up onto Matt's lap, facing him, ready to play. Their game of Timothy falling backward and Matt catching him was a favorite. I was across the kitchen as I saw this unfolding. Since Matt's hands were cuffed behind his back, I flew across the room and slid on my belly along the floor with both hands clasped and outstretched in front of me. I caught Timothy's head just as it crashed onto my hands on the linoleum-covered concrete floor.

"Where's the package?" one officer asked.

I said, "I didn't know what it was when I picked it up, but it was sent here by Matt's brother, and we will give it to our lawyer tomorrow morning to return to you."

The lead officer asked why I wouldn't give it to him right away. But, in the few minutes they had been in our home, two or three officers had already searched some rooms and now were busy ransacking the bedrooms of my older sons, emptying their drawers on the floor, and throwing their things around. I said, "I don't trust you! Look at what your officers are doing to my sons' rooms. I told you I would give you the package. You and your posse have shown my children who you really are by inflicting trauma upon them."

Stomach churning, I was also filled with anxiety for Timothy, who was sick with what I later learned was pneumonia. A house doctor was scheduled to come to examine him that evening. But I wasn't there. I was in jail.

I called friends, who came immediately to care for the children while officers took Matt and me in separate cars to the "Blue Roof Inn"—the beautiful Frank Lloyd Wright building that houses Marin County offices, courtrooms, and jail. Matt was booked for having one marijuana cigarette. He was released shortly thereafter, thanks to Gary Giacomini, our next-door neighbor and our attorney, who was also our County Supervisor. The officer took me to the women's jail and booked me for *smuggling.*

Because smuggling is a federal crime, they then took me to the federal lock-up in San Francisco. It was closed for the night, so they transported me to the county jail instead. I was terrified.

On the way to the San Francisco jail, I talked to the arresting officer about what he and his officers had done. Neither I nor my children had smuggled anything into this country, but he and his gang had come into our home as I was cooking dinner and left chaos in their wake. He listened uncomfortably without responding. I was consumed with anxiety over this ordeal because I didn't know how long I would be in jail and was worried about my sick young son. I also wondered if anyone would be there to meet me at the jail and was wracking my brain to think of who might be able to help me through this ordeal once I arrived.

When a short, dark-haired man fingerprinted me, he squeezed and pressed each of my fingers especially hard onto the black ink pad and then the paper that recorded my prints. Gruff and cruel, he inflicted as much pain as he could on me. Momentarily distracted by a young Black woman who came through the door and greeted the officer by name, he asked her, "What are *you* doing here?"

"I got nabbed by that rookie," she answered.

The officer said, "I told you to watch out for the new rookie on that corner!"

So, the young sex worker was friendly with the jailer, and he was friendly with her. *I* was the stranger in their midst. Lenny Bruce said, "Cops and criminals are on opposite sides of the *same* coin. It's by luck or by chance who lands on which side." I learned that firsthand on that eye-opening night.

A single bare lightbulb lit the area where a female officer led me toward a cell. It was a rectangular space that housed three sets of bunk beds. Three beds were occupied. As the matron walked away after locking me in the cell, one woman asked, "What are you in here for?"

I said, "Smuggling."

"You didn't happen to smuggle anything in here, did you?" one of the women asked hopefully.

"Unfortunately, not," I told her, and we all laughed. Humor helped.

I lay down on the cot and hoped for sleep, but my heart was beating too fast, and my lungs were aching. My stomach was upset, and I could not quiet my mind. I didn't know it at the time, but I was having a panic attack.

It wasn't long before the jailer brought another woman into the cell. As they approached, I couldn't see her face, but recognized the voice. "Sharon?" I said.

"Marilyn?" she responded.

What a coincidence! A few years earlier, when I was still living in San Francisco, I'd helped Sharon—a teenage runaway whom I knew through Lenny Bruce—get off drugs. I had invited Sharon to stay in my home if she wanted to get off drugs, which she did. Sharon was in jail because she had not stayed clean, which distressed me. But her calmness about the situation I was in sure helped me. Her presence was fortuitous because I no longer felt alone.

The next morning, we prisoners were herded into a common room for breakfast. When I saw the gray slop they were serving, any appetite I might have had was gone. Instead of eating, I decided to do my daily practice of Tai Chi (meditation in motion) in a corner of the room, hoping to keep myself centered amid the drama. It didn't take long for two jailers to quickly escort me back to my cell for my own safety. Evidently, several Black women thought I was doing voodoo on them and were about to assault me.

After an hour or so, the same officer who arrested me came to escort me to the federal facilities. He seemed apologetic about his actions and those of his officers the previous evening. I wasn't sure if he really meant it or if he was just trying to shut me up. Either way, I appreciated his new tone.

At the Federal Building, I was put into a tiny holding room. Soon a second woman was put into the room with me. She was a heroin addict going through withdrawal. I thought a massage might help her and asked if she'd like one. I spent the next couple of hours helping her relax as she came down from the drugs in her system. I was grateful to be of service. This was a positive way for me to deal with the anxiety of waiting to find out what was happening as time passed.

Once our attorney delivered the package (a box of chocolates with hashish stuffed into the candy from the bottom) to the officials, I was released from custody and all charges were dropped. As the same officer who arrested me rode in the elevator with me to the first floor, he told me that he hadn't slept all night and he wanted to thank me for talking to him. He had decided to resign from his job. I was surprised to hear it, but I was very happy for him and told him so. He seemed happy, too.

Matt's car had been impounded, so he picked me up in a friend's car. Robbie had loaned it to us so we could take our children to Lake Tahoe for Christmas and Michael's birthday. The children were looking forward to building a snowman and Matt and I needed to get away and put this episode behind us. It was months before I began to relax again. I kept waiting for an unexpected knock at the door, followed by an invasion of brazen officers who would turn our lives upside down again.

I don't think Matt's brother ever understood the depths of the trauma he brought to our family. Yet the experience proved to me that not only was I a strong and resilient woman, but that a power greater than me had put the right people in my path to help me and to be helped by me.

●●●

That summer, Matt and I were married by our friend David Meltzer, who was not only one of the key poets of the Beat generation, but also an ordained minister. The ceremony took place in the backyard of our Woodacre house, overlooking a lovely little creek. This was a happy and productive time for our family. I was consumed by providing my children with an alternative education, the children were thriving, and Matt had his construction work.

Matt wanted to sell our house. He always complained about the early morning traffic when people drove down from the Woodacre hills. Cars stopped at the corner and then accelerated and sped past our house on their way to work. Matt also wanted to travel to Mexico for an adventure before buying another house. He found a job nearby where our whole family could work—putting shakes on the roof and shingles on a house in our neighborhood during the summer so we could save money for this adventure. We were well on our way to having the job done when Michael, Troy, and Kate went back to school. Matt and I completed the work in early December.

Our house sold immediately. We put our things in storage and bought a trailer so small it was almost round. With our van, the trailer, and a camping tent, our family headed for Mexico. We had Christmas Eve dinner in Mexico and celebrated Michael's 13th birthday the following day before heading to Mazatlán, where we stayed for three weeks, recovering from our big job. I mastered enough Spanish to grocery shop and ask for a bathroom. We enjoyed the sunshine and the beach, feeling calmer and more carefree than we had in years.

Then we drove to Mismaloya, a beautiful beach just south of Puerto Vallarta and stayed there for several days before driving down the coast to Tenacatita, a small fishing village. We spent the remainder of our time in Mexico in Barra de Navidad, a lovely coastal town south of Puerto Vallarta.

We parked our trailer on a beautiful white sand beach next to a lagoon a mile out of town, put up the tent and called the place our vacation home. When Troy went into town one day and did not come home for hours, I worried about where he was. He returned with goodies to share from a local bakery where he had worked that day. Then both Michael and Troy got jobs, first at the bakery and then at a restaurant during Mardi Gras, 40 days before Easter—when Mexicans came to Barra de Navidad to celebrate the holiday. Even though Troy was only 10, Mexican culture recognized and rewarded the contributions young people could make, which made an impression on all of us.

In San Patricio, a neighboring village, there was a huge parade. At the climax of the parade, a large framework structure was lit, and all kinds of gadgets and gizmos began spinning, whirling, and shooting this way and that. One of the twirling things that flew off the structure landed on the town's thatch-roofed theater and burned the roof off the building. I was amazed that the locals laughed at the flames and continued to enjoy the celebration. People reacted the same way when a bus would go off the road. Riders would get off the bus, look at it tipped halfway over, and laugh (if no one was hurt).

All those years in California and I'd never seen Mexico. Now it was real, and it was revelatory. We found we loved the lightness of being of the people as well as the cultural importance of family. In fact, those four months were the closest we felt as a family. And the children learned more than they would have in school, where they could easily catch up (and did) when they returned.

I had always had a keen interest in pregnancy, labor, and midwifery. It was during our sojourn in Mexico that I decided to go to school to become a Certified Nurse Midwife. Once certified, I planned to go back to Mexico several months a year to help women with their natural childbirths, which the villagers where we stayed had not yet medicalized.

When we got back from Mexico, a friend allowed us to live in our trailer in her driveway while Matt fixed up her double car garage so that she could rent it out after we left. Experts at improvising, we stayed there until we bought another house. Matt and I slept in the trailer with Timothy, and I cooked in the small trailer kitchen. The three older children slept in the large common space in the garage, where there was space for them to study and for us all to play as Matt transformed the area with his construction skills.

In 1975 we bought a house in Forest Knolls in Marin County, where I still live today.

During the early 1970s, I was an apprenticing lay midwife, attending homebirths with Nan Koehler (my friend from Shire School days) and a couple of local doctors. While all the babies I had been honored to welcome into the world were healthy and beautiful, I worried about births that might not be normal and natural. Would I know what to do? I wanted to become a Certified Nurse Midwife to learn what to do in case of a medical emergency.

Nan had been attending birthing women for more than a decade and was concerned I'd be learning all the troubling, unnecessary interventions used during birth if I took the medical route. She was happy, at least, that I had attended homebirths first so that I knew the difference between midwifery-assisted and medicalized births. I understood what she meant when I thought about the difference between my hospital births (even the differences between doctors and hospitals) and the births I'd attended at home in environments that seemed more conducive to calm and focused deliveries. The mothers were less stressed and fearful, and the fathers felt, and were, welcomed and more included in the process.

It may come as a surprise to some that the United States had (and still has) the highest maternal/child mortality rate among developed countries.[1] As recently as November 18, 2020, the Commonwealth Fund published an issue brief pointing out that obstetrician-gynecologists (ob-gyns) are overrepresented in the U.S. maternity care workforce relative to midwives, and there is an overall shortage of maternity care providers (both ob-gyns and midwives) relative to births.[2] In most other countries, midwives outnumber ob-gyns, and home visits and paid parental leave are standard.[3] Although infant mortality rates have declined from 19.9 deaths per 1,000 live births in 1970 to 5.6 deaths per 1,000 in 2019, the U.S. infant mortality rate still is 71 percent higher than any comparable country's average.[4] And maternal deaths after delivery have actually increased in this time period.

Statistics are just numbers, however. The main reason I was so interested in practicing midwifery was the difference it seemed to make in the beauty and wonder of labor and delivery. Given that the babies I had assisted in entering the world had been healthy and the mothers had normal deliveries, I felt that midwife-assisted natural childbirth and follow-up was best for most mothers and infants. Yet I understood the risks and wanted to be prepared for complications.

When I contacted the University of California's Midwifery School, they told me the requirements included first becoming a Registered Nurse. I would then need to work for a year on a medical-surgical unit and another year on an obstetrical unit before I could apply to the midwifery program. It was a long haul, but I was willing and determined.

The College of Marin School of Nursing had a lottery system, and it was three years before I was accepted. During the years I was waiting, I took classes required for an Associate of Science degree along with some of the courses required in the nursing program. Without a car, I hitch-hiked back and forth to school, which was an acceptable mode of transportation at the time. Happily, in 1977, the year I was accepted to nursing school, my brother bought a new car and gave his car to my mother. She gave me her Volkswagen, for which I am still grateful. Having a car made it much easier to get through the two-year nursing program, which was intense.

During the first year we learned about the body in wellness and the second year we learned about the body in sickness. In the first year, several students were dropped because they were considered inappropriate for nursing. I was never clear about what makes a person "inappropriate" for nursing but lived in fear that this would happen to me, even though I was a diligent student.

Truthfully, the trauma of my arrest for "smuggling" cast a shadow on my expectations, even though the outcome was somewhat positive since the arresting officer left the police force after realizing the consequences of his actions on my family. After having been treated unjustly—suffering physical abuse from my father as a child, abandonment by my husband and children's father, and being arrested—I sometimes automatically expected something bad to happen.

Adding to the stress of being in school, the intensity of working in the hospital with patients for the first time, and home life with four children, made this a challenging time for me. Although I was a master at improvising and multitasking, it took some creativity to bring down the threat of complete chaos to controlled pandemonium, which I could live with.

To become more comfortable in the hospital setting and increase my confidence, I volunteered at the hospital during the summer months between my first and second years of the program, doing whatever tasks were needed, like passing out food trays to the patients and helping the nurses change sheets or transfer patients. By the time I was assigned to the obstetrical unit during my last nursing school rotation, I felt like a nursing "pro." Plus, since I had already birthed four babies of my own and assisted as a midwife, this unit was easy for me. It was a joy to share my experience and knowledge with brand new moms and their precious babies.

●●●

After I witnessed that first circumcision in May 1979, however, something changed inside me.

At first, I was terribly depressed that I had allowed my three sons to go through that trauma. How could I have seen those red, raw little penises and not have known something was terribly wrong? At the time I brought my boys home from the hospital, I thought what I saw was the outcome of a procedure that protected them from something that could threaten their health, although I was not clear on the details of that threat. I was filled with remorse and regret at my ignorance about circumcision.

Later, I got angry. I had been duped, misled, betrayed. Circumcision was not just a little snip to remove excess skin. It was an unnecessary invasive surgical procedure that caused pain both during and after surgery, not to mention the fright to an infant of being taken away from his mother and restrained, strapped to a plastic board, instead of held lovingly on a mother or father's chest.

The circumcision I witnessed was so unnatural, so inhumane, that an experienced physician upon seeing my horrified reaction had said to me, **"There is no medical reason for doing this."**

Why were infants subjected to this invasive surgery in their first few days of life? It made no sense.

I had to find out why circumcision in America was accepted, encouraged, and routine. And, if it was in fact medically unnecessary, I had to let people know so this country could stop harming its most helpless, innocent, newest, and brightest beings.

BECOMING INFORMED: THE CREATION OF NOCIRC (NATIONAL ORGANIZATION OF CIRCUMCISION INFORMATION RESOURCE CENTERS) 1979-1989

Chapter 6

EDUCATING MYSELF ABOUT CIRCUMCISION

Others before me had objected to circumcision, written about it, challenged its merits, organized against it, and I honor their contributions and foresight. But circumcision was barely a topic of discussion in hospitals or doctors' offices in 1979. I had given birth to three sons who were circumcised and had not given it much thought. Why? Because I never understood what the word really meant, and I had never actually seen a circumcision. Given the prevalence of circumcisions performed in the U.S. in the 1970s, I wonder if most parents agreed to surgery to remove their baby's foreskin based on the same ignorance.

Even as a midwife who had helped welcome babies, and who knew the importance of protecting the mother/child bond in the first few days, weeks, and months of a child's life, I had not internalized the trauma and negative aspects of circumcision. The mechanics of routine infant circumcision—invasive surgery with no pain relief, away from the comforting arms of loving parents—was completely counter to the benefits of natural birth in terms of bonding and breastfeeding, in which I fervently believed. How could I have been so uninformed?

It took the shock of witnessing a baby being circumcised to jolt me out of my complacency. I felt that baby's pain in every fiber of my body and to the core of my being, and my life changed forever. I was on a mission, for myself and for that traumatized baby.

But if I was going to speak up against circumcision on babies in the first weeks of life, I had to know what I was talking about. I had to know the answer to why baby boys were routinely circumcised—to why my boys had suffered the pain of circumcision. The doctor who performed the circumcision as we nursing students watched had said to me, **"There is no medical reason for doing this."** So, what was the reason for it?

My research began the day after I first witnessed a circumcision. I wanted to know when babies began to be circumcised and what it meant to cultures that perform it as a religious rite. I wanted to know why it was done when there was no religious or cultural reason. When did it become routine and why? Joe and his brother had not been circumcised because their mother had been told they didn't need to be. Joe had felt embarrassed to tell me that he was intact and had wanted to spare our boys from feeling different. Why? I wanted to know everything.

I went to local libraries, but information was practically nonexistent. Graduating shortly after the circumcision demonstration, I was one of four from our class of 60 students hired by Marin General Hospital. That meant I was able to use the hospital library. Even there, written material on circumcision was sorely lacking.

In my spare time during the year that I worked on the medical/surgical floor (a requirement for acceptance into the midwifery program), I wrote to all the midwives and childbirth educators I knew for information about circumcision. Remember, this was pre-digital revolution technology. It was too expensive to make long distance phone calls outside my area code, and I had to rely on card catalogues and the mail. Considering the amount of cumulative experience in the birthing community, where I had many contacts, I was surprised that most were not addressing the issue. How could that be? *Wasn't choosing to circumcise or preserve your baby's foreskin as important as deciding to bottle or breastfeed your baby?*

I was able to get some information on the subject from childbirth educator Rosemary Romberg in Washington State. It was sketchy, but she had learned enough to save her fifth son from the knife. Her book, *Circumcision: The Painful Dilemma,* did not come out until 1985, but she had been researching it since at least 1978, when *Mothering* magazine published her letter requesting that people send her their circumcision experiences.

●●●

In early 1980, I received a complimentary copy of Edward Wallerstein's incomparable *Circumcision: An American Health Fallacy* from Springer Publishing Company. This was the first book to truly shed light on the practice of medicalized circumcision in English-speaking countries, especially the United States. Of note is that Wallerstein was not a physician. He was a business executive, an industrial engineer, and had experience as a researcher in television, marketing, sociology, economics, education, and health. In other words, he was an outsider and therefore not a stakeholder in the medical establishment.

When they had a son, Wallerstein and his wife had queried their OB about circumcision, even though it was a given in the predominantly Jewish community where he grew up. They were reassured it was the right choice for all the usual reasons. But then, 20 years on, a young couple's concern prompted Wallerstein to do a little research—which ended up taking 12 years. When he began his research at a local branch of the New York Public Library, he found only one book on the subject.

It had been written in 1891 and reprinted in 1974. Even so, the medical information was outdated. Pressing on, he located two other books, both anti-circumcision, but "written with such bias and obvious error as to be totally without merit," he noted in his preface.[5] Wallerstein found hundreds of articles on circumcision in medical libraries, but no books. So, he wrote one himself. His main motivation was to dispel and replace the myths and misinformation surrounding circumcision with facts. Wallerstein's references to the methodological flaws, junk science, and researcher bias used to promote circumcision in scientific journals were stunning, as was his historical context.

I was aware of the Jewish ritual of circumcising boys, with parents often hiring a mohel (ritual circumciser) to perform the rite in their own homes. But I was not aware of why. I learned that circumcision is the physical representation of the covenant between God and Abraham described in the Old Testament (Genesis 17:10-14) to set apart those who believed in God from those who didn't. I had completely missed, however, the mystique associated with circumcision by some Christians. Some of the lore about Jesus's foreskin was bizarre and incredible: for instance, "The relic emitted a wonderful odor which had a strange effect on women;" and "the relic emerged in 12 abbeys simultaneously, including Paris, Bologna, Metz, Nancy, and Antwerp."[6]

When I contacted Reverend Russell Zangger, founder of the Remain Intact Organization of Larchwood, Iowa, for information on the religious significance of circumcision for Christians, he sent me more than 120 references to circumcision in the New Testament that say circumcision is of no value to Christians: e.g., "Circumcision is nothing and uncircumcision is nothing but the keeping of the commandments of God" (1 Corinthians 7:19). Zangger was ahead of his time in speaking out against circumcision as a form of child abuse, whether it was based on religious beliefs or not. It was due to him that I read the Bible to try to understand both the Christian and Jewish perspectives on circumcision.

I learned that circumcision was also practiced by Muslim cultures, although it is not mentioned in the Koran, because Islam considered Abraham to be one of their prophets.

Once you start researching circumcision, you will often read that male circumcision is the oldest known human surgical procedure. In fact, that nugget of information is sometimes used as justification for its continuation in modern times. Archeological evidence dating the practice back to ancient Egyptians in the 23rd century BCE showed adult figures being circumcised. Circumcision was practiced elsewhere in Africa, as well as by the Aboriginal people of Australia and by Pacific Islanders. This ritual was for older children (adolescents) however—not infants—and the practice seemed to be an initiation into manhood and a test of bravery.

I also learned from Wallerstein's book that the frequency of circumcision in the U.S. in 1979 was 85 percent,[7] and that "no other country follows this practice, except where the operation is a religious ritual or puberty rite."[8] In fact, except for Jewish and Muslim countries and most of Africa, South Korea, and the Philippines, it was only English-speaking countries—the U.S., England, Canada, Australia, and New Zealand—that promoted circumcision for non-religious reasons in the nineteenth and twentieth centuries, with the U.S. first introducing nonreligious circumcision around 1870.[9]

Chief among these health considerations regarding circumcision was the fear of physical and emotional illnesses due to masturbation.

At first, I had no idea why medical practitioners thought men who were circumcised were less likely to masturbate. As a nurse, mother, wife, and midwife, I knew boys and men (as well as girls and women) masturbate. In the 1970s, I had helped set up a sex talk hotline for which we educated and trained teens to answer other teens' questions honestly and accurately, with adult back up. What did masturbation have to do with circumcised or intact penises?

It turns out, according to Wallerstein's research, that the fear of masturbation was really about imposing morals about sex on the population of America. I presumed this attitude was influenced by the notably prudish Victorian era, 1837-1901, but it was present even before that in the U.S.

Dr. Benjamin Rush was the only signer of the Declaration of Independence who was a physician. He served as Surgeon General of the Continental Army and was a professor of chemistry, medical theory, and clinical practice at the University of Pennsylvania. Rush believed that nervous energy was the basis of all disease. Since orgasm was one of the most obvious expenditures of such energy, over-indulgence in sex of any kind could result in (according to Rush, quoted in Wallerstein's book) "seminal weakness [excess release of semen], impotence, dysury [pain with urination, most often caused by a urinary tract infection], tabes dorsalis [degenerating nerves in the dorsal columns of the spinal cord], pulmonary consumption [tuberculosis], dyspepsia, dimness of sight, vertigo, epilepsy, hypochondriasis [hypochondria], loss of memory, malangia [melancholy], fatuity [stupidity] and death."[10]

Dr. Rush was a highly respected and prominent leader in the 1700s and 1800s, and his contributions are notable. In 1965, the American Psychiatric Association contributed to a plaque at his gravesite at Christ

Church Cemetery in Philadelphia that called Rush "the father of American psychiatry."[11] But he was wrong to blame orgasm, and particularly masturbation, for so many illnesses. The actual target of circumcising males to prevent or curb masturbation was to decrease their enjoyment of sex and thus preserve the sanctity and sanity of the delicate female, which was obviously a patriarchal concept.

If the APA honored Rush as the father of American psychiatry, I could only conclude that the field needed a mother. I couldn't help thinking, what a load of you-know-what. I realized there was a lot of confusion about the origin of illnesses before the discovery of germs and microbes. Of course, I reached maturity during the Sexual Revolution not the American Revolution. Still, Rush and others who supported the demonization of masturbation as a source of illness, and circumcision as the cure, seemed dimwitted.

I wanted to keep an open mind. Yet the further I got in the Wallerstein book, the more astounded I was at the presumptions and myths on which circumcision was based. I wasn't a doctor; I was a nursing graduate. But I could see the flaws in the conclusions supporting circumcision, and many of them seemed based not only on unscientific studies, but on outdated preconceptions.

Besides being a cure for masturbation, the other prevailing health consideration regarding circumcision was (and still is) that it prevented infections and was more hygienic. Yet if that were true, wouldn't the rest of the world have been practicing circumcision at the same elevated rate as the U.S.? In his chapter on penile hygiene, Wallerstein writes "If the penis is actually such an unhygienic organ, then it should follow that about 75 percent of the world's male population, i.e., those who remain non-circumcised throughout life, must be paying a dreadful price in pain and disease as a result."[12] But they were not.

Wallerstein, writing and researching between 1968 and 1980, found that assumptions about improper penile hygiene were largely based on WWII induction physicals of military recruits.[13] It should be noted that most of these recruits were poor, rural, and minorities, which meant they did not have the same access to hygiene, healthcare, or education as those more well-to-do. This confused the benefits of circumcision with the benefits of social class.[14]

You would find the same problem of more infections due to poor hygiene if you studied dental health. The fact is that those who are not taught to properly care for their own bodies tend not to care for themselves properly. Hygiene is simple to teach, and hygienic care of an intact penis is easy. Amputation of a natural part of the human body is not a sane or satisfactory substitute for education.

Why did post-WWII healthcare professionals ever promote the idea that caring for an intact penis was more difficult than keeping a circumcised penis clean? A penis is simply washed like a finger, from the body outward. No one should try to retract a boy's foreskin prematurely. The first person to retract the foreskin should be the boy himself. He can be taught to retract, rinse with warm water and fingertips (no soap) and replace the foreskin to its forward position. With young children, urinary tract infections (UTIs) may be due to bacteria, which live normally in the digestive tract to help digest food and also are present in poop, getting into the urethra as young boys learning to care for themselves may fail to wash their hands thoroughly after wiping themselves and before touching their foreskin. But that is true for both circumcised and intact boys. What is the problem? Perhaps that Victorian holdover that boys or their mothers shouldn't be touching the penis?

I thought Wallerstein brilliant in his exposé, but this book was making me nuts! His prodigious research revealed that if you approach the issue of circumcision with curiosity and common sense, it is quite literally based on "fallacy," as the title of his book states. Hadn't anyone else in the medical or health field read this book? If so, why was routine infant circumcision still being practiced and justified? I couldn't help but think how ironic (or moronic?) it was to regard our American healthcare system and medical education as the standard for the world when simple truths and basic context were ignored in "scientific" studies on which the benefits of circumcision were based.

Regarding a higher risk of sexually transmitted diseases (STDs) for those with intact penises versus circumcised penises, for example, the first myth was that since Jews had lower rates of venereal diseases and they were circumcised, circumcision prevented STDs. Cultural practices of Orthodox Jews and the fact that up until the twentieth century Jews had often lived in ghettos, cut off from mainstream populations, were not taken into consideration.[15]

One study from 1855 shouldn't carry much weight, I would think, but remember there was very little research available on circumcision, even in the 1970s. And, just like the results based on predominantly poor, rural, and minority WWII enlisted men, the economic and sociocultural backgrounds of the samples were not taken into consideration. The demographics were skewed.

Another myth was that circumcised penises prevent STDs because there is nowhere for germs to hide. Nope. Guess what does make the biggest difference in preventing STDs? Condoms! A study published in

1978 showed that there was a decline in the incidence of gonorrhea in intact men in Sweden, but not in Norway, Denmark, and Finland. The difference was attributed to the promotion of condom use.[16] I guess U.S. doctors and researchers missed that little nugget at the time—but what about over 40 years later? The citation was in Wallerstein's 1980 book! There were other studies over the decades that supported the finding that condoms make a bigger difference in preventing STDs than circumcision.

As I read this carefully researched account of how a few examples of something had been interpreted as evidence of a fact and how context for findings had been ignored in favor of quick conclusions, I felt even more disappointed in "modern" medicine. I couldn't shake the feeling I had on that day in May 1979—something was off with the medical establishment's promotion, collusion, or tolerance of circumcision as a "given."

After immersing myself in Wallerstein's book, I contacted him. Ed, as I came to know him, took me under his wing and became my teacher, mentor, and friend. Other people were helpful as well: Jeffrey Wood, who founded INTACT (Infants Need to Avoid Circumcision Trauma) in Massachusetts; James Peron, a childbirth educator in Pennsylvania; and John Erickson in Mississippi, working to protect babies with his brilliant writing. But Wallerstein's book is what opened my eyes and gave me the foundation of a well-researched argument in favor of foreskin intactness.

The conclusion of *Circumcision: An American Health Fallacy* is that "routine infant health circumcision is archaic, useless, potentially dangerous, and therefore should cease."[17] In addition, Wallerstein placed responsibility for its continued proliferation on the medical profession. "The profession seems to accept circumcision as a 'national cultural trait' as much as do lay people. With evidence at hand to disprove the prophylactic benefits of the surgery, the medical profession has the responsibility to discourage this practice. The pretense of neutrality is a negative stance."[18] It also makes healthcare professionals complicit.

Incredibly, this seems almost as true today as it was when Wallerstein's book was written over 40 years ago. The rate of circumcision among infants born in the hospital has decreased, but it is far from comparable to European countries.

Thanks to Wallerstein's research, I knew more than I did before but still had no idea why this country continued to embrace a practice that our peer countries had abandoned. All I knew was that every parent has a right and an obligation to know the truth about non-therapeutic neonatal circumcision and what would happen to their baby during a "surgery," often euphemistically called a "procedure," that is invasive, painful, traumatizing, and unnecessary.

How could I clarify for parents what circumcision really is—an expectation of cultural conformity that has nothing to do with health? The evidence I had read since I began my quest for knowledge about circumcision was as clear as the words the doctor had said to me when I was a nursing student trying to comfort an anguished infant: **"There is no medical reason for doing this."**

Could the solution be as simple as recommending Wallerstein's book to everyone I knew? It was hardly bedtime reading, but surely medical professionals should know about it. My role was to keep reading and researching, and to pass along my knowledge to parents in objective, non-judgmental, conversational language appropriate to the hospital setting.

I would learn that educating parents was a conundrum of epic proportions that was not for the faint of heart.

Chapter 7

PARENTAL EDUCATION OR PARENTAL COERCION?

After I had worked on the medical/surgical unit at the hospital for a year, I transferred to the obstetrical unit. As I cared for postpartum mothers and their babies, I kept researching and learning more about circumcision.

Up to this point, I had been very careful about what I shared regarding my research on circumcision with the medical staff at Marin General Hospital. I had seen how unfair the administration could be when it came to firing employees. Soon after I had started working on the medical/surgical unit, I was promoted to night charge nurse due to an unexpected staffing change. Unprepared for my new responsibilities, I would have floundered except for a wonderful aide who had been working at the hospital for many years. She helped me learn the job and kept me grounded during that trying year. This amazing woman cared for her husband, who had lost a leg during WWII, during the day and worked all night at the hospital. When the hospital was privatized, she was let go just months before she was qualified to retire and receive the retirement benefits she had earned after all her years of service. This shocked me to the core. I became more guarded about my interactions after that.

The more I found out about the facts surrounding circumcision, however, the harder it was to keep it to myself. Working on the OB unit, I was more comfortable sharing information with other night nurses, who were learning, too. After all, this was, you might say, ground zero for making the circumcision decision. My nursing colleagues came to understand why I was passionate about educating others and providing information to parents so they could make an informed decision.

Nurses were responsible for taking the babies scheduled for circumcision to their mothers at 6am for a last feeding before surgery. The reason was to give babies two hours to digest the food so that when they screamed and choked from pain during circumcision, there wouldn't be any vomit for them to inhale.

Nurses were also responsible for taking the circumcision consent form to the new mothers for their signatures. In nursing school, we were taught the importance of obtaining *informed consent* for any surgical procedure. We were told that it was our job to ensure the person signing the consent form had all the necessary information needed to make a truly informed decision. This included understanding the reason(s) for surgery, what happens during the surgery, and the risks and benefits of the procedure. In addition, patients should always be told about alternatives to any proposed surgery, such as non-surgical treatment for a particular disease or condition, and, always, the option of "non-intervention"—in other words, doing nothing.

The problem with informed consent is obvious when the proposed surgery is to remove a normal, healthy body part from a non-consenting baby. There is no disease and the person signing the consent form isn't the person having the surgery, absorbing the risks, and living with the lifelong consequences. In medical ethics, parental consent *or assent*—a form of "surrogate" consent—is considered valid only to ensure the life or health of a child. The foreskin is not a birth defect; it's a normal part of the penis, has protective and immunological properties, and contributes greatly to sensual and sexual pleasure.

None of these things were mentioned in the general surgery consent form we gave to mothers for their signature at Marin General Hospital. The most one could say for the consent form is that it might insulate the hospital from liability should the baby be injured or the mother claim later that she was coerced or deceived into consenting.

One baby after another was circumcised and parents didn't have a clue about what their babies were experiencing during the procedure. I began providing accurate information so that when parents signed a consent form, they were truly informed. Due to my sharing what I was learning, other nurses were doing this too, each in their own way.

First, I would ask what the mother knew: for example, I would say "I have a consent form here for your baby's circumcision, which you will need to sign. May I ask why you have decided to have your baby circumcised?"

The answers varied somewhat but often it was, "Because it's cleaner and healthier."

If that was a mother's response, I would ask, "Did you know that the American Academy of Pediatrics says that soap and water offer all the advantages of circumcision without the risks of surgery?"

"Circumcision is surgery?" the mother would invariably ask. When I said it was, a mother often asked about anesthesia. I would tell the truth—babies were not anesthetized for circumcision. Even today, after the harmful effects of pain and trauma to the baby's developing brain and body are well documented, about half of the babies in the United States still are circumcised without anesthesia.

"Do babies cry?" mothers would ask.

I answered honestly, "Yes, they do because circumcision is painful."

Some mothers might justify their decision to circumcise their baby by saying, "It's because we're Christians." I would ask if they knew there are more than 120 references to circumcision in the New Testament that say circumcision is of no value to Christians. Most didn't, of course, and some even admitted to never having read the Bible. I couldn't judge them because neither had I before my interaction with Reverend Zangger. I'd go on to explain that Christ was meant to be the last blood sacrifice and that, for Christians, it was not outward signs (genital cutting) that mattered, but faith expressed through love.

One mother told me her son was being circumcised because she is a Jew. I asked why he was being circumcised on the third day by a doctor in the hospital and not on the eighth day with a mohel performing the ceremony. "Will his circumcision satisfy the covenant?" I asked.

"What's the covenant?" was her response.

Again, I didn't judge these mothers because I knew that many religious rituals were cultural rather than religious. But it was disturbing to me that any religion was used as a rationale for infant surgery when those making that decision for a baby's body did not have a clue about what circumcision stood for in their religious philosophy.

Some parents told me they wanted their son circumcised to match his father. I would ask, "If your husband was missing a foot, an eye, or an appendix, would you want your son to bear the same losses and the same scars?" I wonder why it is that when we get to the genitals, we lose our capacity to be reasonable.

One morning, Linda Duffy, the nurse in charge of the obstetrical unit, told me a mother had complained about a nurse who made her feel guilty for circumcising her baby. I said, "None of the nurses on our shift would do that, Linda. Did she say who the nurse was?" I was shocked to learn the mother had complained about *me.* I said, "Linda, as the mother of three circumcised boys, I would *never* say anything to make a mother feel guilty. My job is to provide facts so that, when a mother signs the consent form, she is truly informed."

Linda had been a midwife in the UK, where circumcision is no longer routinely done, and she told me the first time she saw a circumcision, she blurted out, "That's bloody barbaric." She said that I needed to be very careful, though, because circumcision was a sensitive subject at Marin General.

Following her advice, I walked on eggshells. But I knew I had a legal responsibility and a moral obligation to say what I could to provide mothers with accurate information. I told them what I wish I had been told.

Many babies were spared because their mothers and fathers asked questions and were given honest answers. But many parents went forward with circumcision even after I explained the procedure. Beyond religious reasons, I wondered why parents still chose to subject their babies to pain and trauma even after I explained that circumcision was not medically necessary. What was it they weren't getting, and what could I do to help them better understand? I only had the window of opportunity that came with the obligation to explain the surgery when they were presented with the consent form. It wasn't much time to present truthful information, like the newsflash to most that it is not medically necessary, and to answer their questions. Looking back, I suppose the reason parents still chose circumcision was cultural conditioning and the fact that it was not a doctor who was telling them these facts about a surgery they thought was a quick procedure with the pain quickly forgotten.

As a result of the complaint filed against me, the hospital changed the process of getting the consent forms signed by mothers. The task of having the forms signed was transferred to the evening-shift nurses. Unlike the night nurses on my shift, who now were educated and provided accurate information, the evening nurses were still ignorant about the issue. Our legal obligation to provide accurate information for an informed consent, I suspected, was being undermined purposely. Once again, parents would not be given the facts.

Clinical nurse specialist Pat Lord took me aside to tell me that parents needed to speak to their doctors about circumcision during their pregnancy, that they were too sensitive at the time of birth or afterward to discuss circumcision. I told her I agreed with her, that she was undoubtedly right. But, I said, "Most parents learn nothing about circumcision during their pregnancies. If they don't have the information when they arrive at the hospital, this is their last opportunity to be truly informed before they agree to a surgery for their baby that they might later regret." I added, "Getting upset about the truth of circumcision is the correct response, Pat. We should all be upset about it."

Later I was asked by Pat to head a committee to create an educational handout on circumcision for parents. She may have thought it would keep me busy and, once completed, it would become the "approved" circumcision message at MGH. The committee consisted of several nurses and doctors. I wrote a draft for the handout and introduced it to committee members as a starting point.

I listed the risks of circumcision as hemorrhage, infection, surgical mishap, and, while rare, even death. The doctors objected. I should say "bleeding" instead of hemorrhage and I should not mention death, they said. I argued that babies have indeed died hemorrhaging after circumcision, and from infection or other complications. The truth, however, was not to be told in the Marin General Hospital handout.

There were many points of contention, and it was a difficult process. While we ended up with a watered-down, less than honest or accurate handout, it was better than the previous lack of any educational information whatsoever. The handout was used by the hospital for years after I was "asked" to resign. The hospital later took credit for creating it. That was fine with me because the final version withheld important information and I didn't want to be complicit or credited for contributing to a less than honest handout.

● ● ●

One quiet night at the hospital, my friend and colleague Sheila Curran, who was working in labor and delivery, came to the postpartum unit to chat. Already an accomplished photographer, Sheila was trying to work her way out of nursing and into video production. She mentioned needing a topic for her next filmmaking project.

I had often thought that if parents were able to witness a circumcision, hear the screams, and realize what was going to happen to their baby, they would say "NO!" Hearing a baby's screams alerts our reptilian brain to danger and prompts our heart to respond. I, of course, suggested circumcision as the topic of Sheila's next video, and offered to help. I was thrilled when she agreed.

Around the time we began to work on the video, we were delighted to see the December 1981 issue of *The Saturday Evening Post*, which featured two articles on circumcision. In "Health Groups Conclude Routine Circumcision Not Recommended," Cory SerVaas, MD, quoted the 1971 statement of the Committee on Fetus and Newborn of the American Academy of Pediatrics: "There are no valid medical indications for circumcision in the neonatal period," and the 1975 statement, in which the committee found *no basis for changing their earlier statement*. The full-page, color photos of a screaming baby boy strapped onto a Circumstraint made it glaringly obvious that the baby was suffering. One caption read, "Perhaps if expectant parents knew more about it, they would not subject their newborn infants to circumcision."[19]

In the concluding paragraph of the other article, "The Case Against Newborn Circumcision," Carl Otten, MD, wrote this: "In the eyes of the physician, this barbaric tradition of unnecessary surgery is a thing of the past and should take its place in history books as one of the many traditions that a human civilization has outgrown."[20]

What a refreshing, ethical, and moral perspective. I wished the doctors at Marin General Hospital were so open, wise, and willing to live up to their oath to "do no harm."

By autumn of 1981, Sheila and I had completed the treatment for our video. Sheila asked Dr. Edward Boyce, one of the attending obstetricians, if he would allow us to videotape him doing a circumcision. Ed knew our position on the issue, and he agreed. Sheila got the video crew together and hospital permission to bring the crew into the newborn nursery. Sheila's first video about stress tests for pregnant women was informative and well done. Our supervisors had appreciated her video and that probably helped them trust our current effort.

Because one of the mothers in the hospital was Dr. Boyce's patient, I could speak frankly with her about circumcision. She asked educated questions and was well informed. She didn't want to circumcise her son, but it was important to her husband, and she acquiesced. Knowing I'd done all I could and that this baby would be circumcised no matter what I said, I asked the mother's permission to videotape the procedure. She signed both the consent and the release forms.

In the nursery, the lights were on, and the camera was rolling. The two-day-old infant was struggling against restraints that held him spread-eagle to the Circumstraint circumcision board. His whimpering was becoming more and more distressed until the nurse began swabbing his penis with dark orange Betadine antiseptic solution. The baby became quiet and attentive to this new sensation. His penis did what penises normally do when stimulated, it became erect. The nurse scrubbed for several minutes 'round and 'round that little penis, which maintained its stiffness.

With scrubbed hands, Doctor Boyce arrived and took his place in front of the baby, whose lower body was covered by a surgical drape with a small hole in it. The baby's little erect penis poked through that hole. The doctor began, and the baby screamed and screamed throughout the 15-minute ordeal.

While this was not the first circumcision I had witnessed, it was the first time the link between sex and violence was horrifyingly clear to me. Babies have erections naturally in utero. After birth, when someone else stimulates the baby's penis to erection, as the nurse had done in her prep for the circumcision, it is the baby's *first shared sexual experience*. Sadly, in the case of circumcision, the pleasurable sensations are immediately followed by excruciating pain. Every sexual experience a circumcised male has from that moment forward is on a neuronal background of pain. Even when a man doesn't consciously remember the experience, his body remembers.

As we were videotaping, doctors who were making morning rounds stood looking through the nursery window, shaking their heads. Since the door to the nursery was open, I could hear them asking one another, "Why would anyone want to videotape *that?*" To educate parents about what you do to their precious babies behind closed doors, I thought. I knew all too well that to describe what would happen versus seeing a circumcision were two very different experiences.

With help from my son Troy, who narrated the video, Sheila and I completed our 20-minute educational video, *Informed Consent*. We proudly sent invitations for our premier to every nurse and doctor who worked on the obstetrical, postpartum, and neonatal intensive care units, the pediatric ward, the nursing and hospital administrators, along with family, friends, and concerned individuals. The screening was held at Marin General Hospital one evening in 1982.

Only one nurse and one doctor from our hospital came to our screening, despite the convenience of the location and the importance of the subject matter. That was our first lesson of just what we were up against: the status quo, apathy, arrogance, and indifference. We were dealing with not only the medical establishment but the cultural stance of our entire country regarding circumcision.

As the video played and the first scream came out of the baby's mouth, my husband Matt, who had not seen the video until then, leapt to his feet and cried out, "Jesus Christ!" Then he proceeded to pace back and forth for the next 15 minutes as the video revealed the truth of a baby's experience during his circumcision. On the way home, Matt said, "And, to think I agreed to circumcising my son because I thought a circumcised penis looks better." He shook his head and dropped it into his hands.

I remember saying, "We didn't know what circumcision was then. Now we do!" I have said those words thousands of times since that evening as parents have expressed their profound grief, regret, and remorse to me over the years.

Since the OBs hadn't come to see our video, Sheila took it to the doctors' monthly meeting. I was out of town at the time, running the last part of a marathon with my brother as he was finishing his first Iron Man Triathlon in Hawaii. When I returned and Sheila told me what had happened, I was sorry she had to face the doctors alone. Sheila said the doctors acted like a pack of dogs—from little yappers to Rottweilers.

The doctors claimed we made the baby's screams louder when, in fact, we had tried to soften them because it was hard to hear the doctor's voice with the sound of the baby's screams. They claimed we had added blood to make it look worse than it was. We had *not*. It is extremely difficult to sit and watch a baby being tortured and mutilated in color on a full screen as you clearly witness the baby's struggle and desperate reactions to the traumatic experience. The doctors were more comfortable denying reality and blaming us than recognizing the suffering they were inflicting on newborn babies.

Our video was shown at Marin General Hospital in 1982 in two of Margaret Farley's childbirth education classes. Six male babies were born to parents from the first class and not one was circumcised. Success! Four of the five baby boys born to parents who came to the second class were kept intact. The fifth boy was the son of a Jewish physician who practiced at the hospital. When he complained about our video being shown at the hospital, it was censored by Pat Lord, the Clinical Nurse Specialist. Remarkably, she told Margaret she could show *Informed Consent* in any of her other childbirth classes but not at her Marin General Hospital Childbirth Education classes.

When Sheila and I had first shown our video to Pat Lord (who had not come to our hospital premier), she said, "Now *girls,* I would want to stop the video here and say to parents, 'See how the baby frets when he's strapped down?'"

I asked, "Pat, are you telling me you do not hear the difference in the sounds the baby makes when he's strapped down and the sounds he makes as someone amputates thousands of nerve endings from his penis without anesthesia?" She didn't respond. But it was obvious she had a double standard when it came to circumcision. The video was appropriate for Margaret to show in her other childbirth classes but not at MGH. Clearly, Pat was protecting the hospital, the doctors, the status quo, and the parents—but not the babies.

After the video was censored by Pat, Sheila and I asked the hospital's Ethics Committee to view it. We hoped they would support Margaret showing it to her hospital childbirth classes. We met with committee members in a hospital conference room. They sat silently as they watched our video. Then one of the committee members asked why we had made the video and who had paid for it. We said we had made it to educate parents so that they could make a truly informed decision. We had paid for it ourselves. Several members commended us for taking the initiative and stated their appreciation of our efforts. But they did nothing as far as we could tell to reverse the censorship decision. The video never again was shown in childbirth classes at Marin General.

That didn't deter Sheila and me. In fact, we were just getting started. Word was getting out about our video, and we were marketing it to childbirth educators, midwives, informed physicians, parents, lawyers, and concerned individuals. Our video brought circumcision into the light. As more parents became informed and educated, many of them were saying "No!" to circumcision.

I suggested to one of my patients that she watch *Informed Consent* prior to her son's circumcision. The next day she checked out with her circumcised baby, and she took our unwatched video home with her. A couple of weeks later, I wrote to ask her to return our video, which she did with a note. She thanked us for sharing the video with her, saying she and her husband were grateful to have seen what had happened to their baby, and happy to know it was such an easy surgery.

How could the parents listen to a distressed baby screaming in pain for 15 minutes and conclude circumcision was an easy surgery? Were we on different planets?

That was when something clicked and I realized that *circumcision is not an informed consent issue, it is a human rights issue.* No matter how much information you offer, some people will be able to ignore what they hear and see because they feel entitled to make the decision they want to make on behalf of another human being.

My first response to circumcision was one of compassion for the baby. I physically felt the baby's pain. After educating myself, my response was based on evidence that it was an unnecessary surgery. Now I was beginning to understand that cutting a healthy body part off a non-consenting infant or child—irrespective of the parent's consent—is a violation of the child's most basic human right, the right to bodily integrity and genital autonomy (personal choice). Circumcision is irreversible. When I failed to protect my sons from circumcision, their right to their own bodies and self-determination were denied. As I became more familiar with the risks and consequences of circumcision, the human rights aspect would clarify, as would my mission.

Chapter 8

UNDERSTANDING, ENGAGEMENT, ACTION

Sheila and I had invited ABC radio talk-show host and television medical anchorman Dr. Dean Edell to attend the 1982 screening of our *Informed Consent* video at MGH. I had been listening to Dr. Edell since the 1970s and was always impressed by his ability to make medical jargon understandable to the public. He was attuned to trending topics, and I hoped he would be interested in what we were doing. Unable to attend our screening, Dean invited us to bring our *Informed Consent* video to the ABC studios in San Francisco.

We were encouraged when he acknowledged and applauded our efforts. But he did more than that. Our video was well done, he noted, but it wasn't TV broadcast quality. We were excited when Dean asked if we would be willing to help him create a more technically advanced media savvy mini-documentary for his show. What a wonderful opportunity for us to reach more people!

The documentary aired during the medical segment of the six o'clock news on two consecutive nights in 1982. Although Dean's television segment was local to the San Francisco Bay area, it was a great way to break into the media spotlight. He was respected and respectful, and his team was top-notch.

When Dean's camera crew came to interview me at the hospital, they videotaped the bumper stickers on a line of nurses' cars parked outside the emergency room entrance for an interesting visual to add to the story. For safety and convenience, night employees parked in the ER lot, along with emergency room patients, laboring women, and doctors entering the hospital at night. The bumper stickers (sent to us by Rev. Zangger) read, "We are helping STOP routine infant circumcision." No one had ever complained, and we had gotten some great comments from people who wanted to support the cause and/or learn more.

Dean's mini-documentary was the first time circumcision was shown on television in the San Francisco Bay Area. It was clear that cutting a part of a baby's body off without an anesthetic was extremely painful and traumatic. The truth about foreskin amputation was out now and people were talking about the issue. Dean had helped bring attention to the issue and our work, too.

By that time, I was appearing on local TV shows and speaking on radio programs. My fellow nurses were proud of me, but the Marin General doctors were becoming more confrontational. One morning a doctor approached me as I walked toward the nursery and said, "Hey, Marilyn, I'm getting ready to do a circ—a girl today. Do you want to come and hold *her* down?"

I was horrified, but could find no words for him except, "What a sick thing to say to me."

Incidents like these were balanced by good news: there was increasing interest in stopping infant circumcision and there were more opportunities for education.

On the personal front, I welcomed my first grandson, Matthew, into the world a few days before Thanksgiving in 1982. He was the first member of my immediate family to benefit from my mission of educating parents about the reality of circumcision. I was flooded with relief and gratitude that this precious little boy was safe from the ordeal of circumcision. Kate knew she wanted to protect Matthew and, after watching our video, Matthew's dad readily agreed to protect his son, too.

Because Pat Lord had banned the use of our video in Marin General's childbirth classes, I needed another way to show it to mothers and fathers who were considering circumcision for their sons. Dr. Boyce, who had allowed us to videotape the circumcision for *Informed Consent,* supported our outreach by writing orders for his patients to watch the video. This way, I could pop our video into the VCR in a patient's hospital room without the risk of being fired. I was so grateful that one doctor, at least, was supportive of sharing our efforts to make sure parents made a truly informed decision.

As I watched one mother with her baby in her arms, sobbing while viewing *Informed Consent*, I thought, "Oh what have I done? She's so upset." When the video was over, I apologized for the pain it had caused her.

She said, "It was horrible to watch, but I'm so grateful I did. There is no way we are going to sign that consent form!"

Those parents, like many others, thanked me again and again before departing for home with their intact baby. As you can imagine, these were joyous occasions for me. I was always delighted when I was able to educate parents who then protected their sons.

I also tried to keep in mind that even if it seemed I had "failed" in my efforts, I had perhaps planted a seed that would bear fruit in the future. Sometimes parents weren't ready to let go of what they thought they knew or wanted. But as my little corner of the country became more aware—through Sheila's and my efforts and those of Dean Edell and a few others—of what circumcision was and its consequences, things would change.

●●●

Up until I helped with Dean Edell's mini-documentary, my focus had been on researching and studying circumcision to educate myself, other healthcare workers, and parents about the lack of medical reasons for the surgery. My belief that circumcision caused pain and suffering for an infant had been substantiated. What I did not know about and had not considered was the ongoing trauma of circumcision in the life of a male, whether a school-age child, a teenager, or an adult. As I began to participate in more media opportunities to educate the public about circumcision, men who felt like "survivors" of circumcision started to contact me.

Pablo de la Rosa (aka Paul Eastman) was the first man to write to me about his lifelong emotional response to circumcision: *"I was circumcised when I was five—70 years ago. I felt rage then and I still feel rage today."*

Another note I received that I have never forgotten was from a father who wrote this lament: "*What was so difficult in leaving my son intact was not that my son would feel different in a locker room, but that I would feel different from him. I would then have to accept that I'm an amputee from the wars of a past generation.*"

One man wrote this:

Beginning at the age of eight, I went to a summer camp and, while skinny dipping, was vaguely aware that there were two types of penises, and that the majority were like mine. I never gave this matter much thought until the eighth grade when I began to be curious about sexual matters. One night, as my roommate and I were getting ready for bed, I asked why some penises were different from ours. He told me that every boy is born with a piece of skin covering the end of his penis, but that most of us had ours cut off when we were babies. To say that I was stunned and outraged by this revelation would be an understatement. I simply could not believe that this had happened to me, and I wished that I had been left intact even though I would have been in the minority.

In the last analysis, stopping circumcision is a matter of human rights. Since we cannot predict at birth which males will grow up to resent being circumcised and which will not, the procedure ought to be made illegal until a male reaches adulthood and can choose for himself if he wants to be circumcised.

Hypnotherapy or psychotherapy helped some men remember their circumcision. These therapies often began as part of a healing process for various emotional disorders or traumatic events that had been attributed to other causes having nothing to do with infant or childhood circumcision. For some, the trauma was brought to light when they first became cognizant of being circumcised.

What I learned from the men who shared their experiences with me was that *every man who has a scar on his penis also has a scar on his psyche.*

After I had appeared on several television shows in the Bay Area, Bud Berkeley, editor and publisher of *Foreskin Quarterly* magazine, and co-author with Joe Tiffenbach of *Foreskin: Its Past, Its Present &....Its Future?* (1983), learned about my work and befriended me—the nurse who had begun speaking out against routine circumcision. (Bud's second book, *Foreskin: A Closer Look,* published in 1993, was an expanded and updated edition of his first book.) Bud introduced me to people in the San Francisco gay community who taught me more than I ever expected to learn about penises and the harmful short- and long-term consequences of circumcision.

It was the Gay Revolution and gay men were coming into their own, coming out to their families and the community at a time when the backlash was not friendly. They were organizing for the right to live their lives in the open and were supporting each other as they came out of hiding into the light. As they shared their own experiences, as well as anecdotes from other men, with me, and what they were witnessing at bath houses and other safe spots for the gay culture, they brought a new level of understanding to the circumcision debate.

Besides the emotional damage, they talked to me about ugly scarring, especially from the Gomco clamp that allows blood to seep into the peripheral tissue of the penis, leaving large dark patches under the skin. They told me about tight cuts causing painful erections and loose cuts that helped prevent painful erections, at least somewhat. They told me about curvature of the penis, something that occurs when more skin is taken from one side than the other. They told me about skin bridges and the hunks and slices missing from the glans.

In the beginning, what we knew about the trauma of circumcision was anecdotal. When men wanted to tell me about their deeply felt experiences regarding this body modification of their most sensitive organ, I was both honored and horrified to hear their stories. These brave souls made me even more determined to continue my mission to educate everyone about the consequences of this medically unnecessary surgery.

● ● ●

Around this time, the groundwork was being laid for a field called Birth Psychology, the study of our earliest experiences: in the womb, during birth, and throughout infancy. Dr. Thomas Verny, a Canadian psychiatrist, published his book *The Secret Life of the Unborn Child* in 1981. Dr. David Chamberlain, a California psychologist, had been using hypnotherapy to discover and resolve traumas arising in the womb and at birth and had done research demonstrating that birth memories were reliable memories. These pioneers changed our thinking about babies before and after birth. Thomas Verny founded the Pre- and Peri-natal Psychology Association of North America (PPPANA) in 1983, a community of birth educators, practitioners, and researchers. A few years later, the name was changed to the Association for Prenatal and Perinatal Psychology and Health (APPPAH), and David Chamberlain took the position of president.[21]

The APPPAH website, birthpsychology.com, states this important nugget, which doctors who performed circumcision had been ignoring: "For most of recorded history, it has been believed that babies were not capable of thinking, feeling, or having their own experiences before birth or even for many months afterward; however, we now know babies do **have their own thoughts, feelings, and experiences** even before birth."[22]

Any mother of my generation or before—those who used cloth diapers and diaper pins—will remember with heart-stopping anxiety her baby's shriek when she accidently pricked him while changing his diaper. *Of course, babies feel pain! They are human beings. How could those in the medical profession ever think otherwise?*

Nonetheless, researchers have been compelled to prove the obvious when it comes to circumcision. "There's absolutely no evidence to support the notion that infants don't feel pain," said Fran Porter, a research associate in pediatrics at St. Louis Children's Hospital. "And now we have evidence that refutes that idea."[23] Porter and Dr. Richard Marshall et al. studied 50 healthy male infants who were circumcised without anesthesia. Porter described how the cries of babies being circumcised changed dramatically, becoming shorter, more rapidly repeated, and more frantic as the process went on. "We now know that babies are not physiologically protected against painful stimuli," Porter said. "Although their nerves are to some extent immature and the organization of their nervous system may also be immature, we should not assume that it's not processing information."[24] There is a mountain of evidence that forces us to conclude that newborns who are circumcised without an anesthetic experience pain, including these indicators: increased blood pressure, increased heart rate, decreased oxygen in the blood, and a surge of stress hormones.[25]

If we were talking about female genital mutilation in a country where that practice is considered inhumane, would pain or the use of anesthesia be the issue? These amputations of normal body parts on minor children by adults are human rights violations. Basic human rights are genderless. Every infant and child deserves our protection when we can safeguard them from a medically unnecessary surgery that is nothing more than a cultural custom.

In the early years of my quest for information, I was frustrated that things that are obvious to mothers—like the fact that babies do feel pain—were discounted. I understood that medicine is a constantly developing science and that studies had to prove these things. What was mind-boggling was that a mountain of evidence that proved babies do feel pain could be minimized, deferring to the need to *do more studies.* Denial is a powerful impulse I learned—over and over. What else can explain the insistence of a circumcising physician or the assisting nurse that the baby's agonized screams, choking, and eventual descent into silent shock only reflect his discomfort with being immobilized?

●●●

In 1983 I was contacted by Richard Morris, a California attorney who wanted to file the first circumcision lawsuit to raise the question: Does a parent have the legal power to consent to a surgical procedure that has no medical purpose?

I asked local midwives and childbirth educator Margaret Farley to let people know I was looking for a plaintiff. Margaret gave my phone number to Trudie London, a doctor's wife, who contacted me when she learned I was looking for a plaintiff in a circumcision lawsuit. Trudie had not wanted her son circumcised but conceded to her Jewish husband's wishes. She insisted, however, that her son's umbilical cord heal prior to his circumcision, which gave her time to get to know her baby.

When Trudie and her husband took their son to the physician's office for circumcision, they were told to take a walk around the block. Upon their return, Trudie realized her son was not the same baby she had left just 15 minutes earlier. Her baby was peaceful and content when she left him. When she returned, he was agitated, fussy, and she could see by the wrinkles in his brow that he was upset in a way he'd never been before. She recognized the adverse effects of pain and trauma inflicted on her baby and wondered why she had been lied to by the doctor about the pain and harmful consequences of circumcision.

With Richard Morris and Jeannette Edell as her attorneys, Trudie filed a lawsuit in 1984 as guardian ad litem on behalf of her son. It was time to legally challenge the medical establishment.

The first judge to make a ruling in the lawsuit granted Trudie's son, the plaintiff, two causes of action—battery and false imprisonment. The second, a Superior Court judge, clearly didn't, couldn't, or wouldn't understand the issue because he said, in effect, since circumcision is the oldest surgery known to man, and because of the court's reluctance to interfere in family life, he found in favor of the defendant—the doctor. Following his ruling and absent a successful appeal of the decision, the genitals of every child, both boys and girls, would not be protected or safe in the state of California.

As the appeal was being filed, I wrote my first newsletter. I wanted to keep the people who had donated to the lawsuit fund informed. The appeal was now proceeding through the California court system. The wheels of justice turn slowly, and the Appellate Court judges would not hear the case until the following year. We would have to wait.

●●●

Once I had met the requirements for midwifery school—working one year on a medical/surgical unit and one year on an obstetrical unit—I began applying again. I was told it, like nursing school, was a lottery system and it probably would take five years for me to be accepted. Although disappointed, I was neither surprised nor deterred by not being accepted the first two years I applied.

As I began working on my third application, a midwife and instructor at the midwifery school who knew about my work invited me to come to the school to speak to her class. While I was talking to the students, I realized I was speaking to the nurses who had been accepted that year instead of me. I knew I was doing what I needed to do and realized then that I was on a mission.

I spoke with the administrator of the midwifery school. I said I was working to end routine infant circumcision. I told her I thought it would take me two years to complete the task, and I wondered if the two years I'd already applied would still count if I did my work first and then came back and applied again. She assured me it would.

Because I was off in my estimate—circumcision did not end in two years—I never did re-apply to midwifery school. I was already doing my best to assure a safe and natural entry for infants into the world and I would not rest until the harmful consequences of circumcision were on the radar of every parent and healthcare provider and the beneficial aspects of remaining intact were known as well.

● ● ●

While the first circumcision lawsuit was being filed in California, the American Academy of Pediatrics published its 1984 brochure, authored by my dear Ed Wallerstein, *Care of the Uncircumcized*[sic] *Penis.* It was revised within months to correct the AAP's misspelling of the word *uncircumcised*.

Ed's original text for the brochure included the following section, under the heading, "The Function of the Foreskin":

The glans at birth is delicate and easily irritated by urine and feces. The foreskin shields the glans; with circumcision, this protection is lost. In such cases, the glans and especially the urinary opening (meatus) may become irritated or infected, causing ulcers, meatitis (inflammation of the meatus), and meatal stenosis (a narrowing of the urinary opening). Such problems virtually never occur in uncircumcised penises. The foreskin protects the glans throughout life.

The AAP's next revision of the brochure left out this critical information.

On May 6, 1986, I wrote to the AAP:

We have just received a copy of your revised edition of Care of the Uncircumcised Penis. Deletion of the section entitled, "The Function of the Foreskin" is apparent. We are wondering if there is new evidence that the foreskin, in fact, does not provide protection for the sensitive glans. Furthermore, we are wondering if its removal does not cause the problems of irritation, infection, ulceration, meatitis, and meatal stenosis as originally reported in your 1984 edition of this brochure.

In response, I received a letter from Jean D. Lockhart, MD, Director of Maternal, Child and Adolescent Health for the AAP saying, in part: *"The revisions were done by our Section on Urology, in the interest of brevity. Our policy on circumcision has not changed."*

Because of the extended white space in the brochure caused by omission of this important paragraph, I wrote back, taking issue with "in the interest of brevity." Lockhart, in turn, directed me to George Kaplan, MD, who, I was told, had a hand in the revision. So, on June 9, I wrote to Dr. Kaplan, asking the same question.

His July 10th reply noted that the major reason for the deletion was that it did not contribute to the purpose of informing and educating pediatricians and parents who decided their children should not be circumcised. Additionally, he wrote that to the best of his knowledge **there was no information available about the function of the foreskin.**

What?

I knew Kaplan's answer skirted my questions but wasn't yet aware of just how far the American Academy of Pediatrics or its representatives were willing to go to keep the truth from the public and to protect circumcision advocates and practitioners.

I had no idea how deeply the practice of circumcision had infiltrated the psyche of Americans and how reactive some people would be to receiving accurate information about it. During my years on the MGH postpartum unit, many parents thanked me for providing them with new information, which helped them to make the decision to protect their sons. During that same five-year period, many mothers I spoke to kindly and politely thanked me for the information but still chose to circumcise their babies.

Three mothers, however, wrote complaints about me.

The first complaint was made by a Jewish woman who told me she was afraid of not being a good mother because she was unable to console her newborn baby. I asked if he had been circumcised that morning. When she said he had, I explained that her son's reaction to his circumcision was typical and that his inconsolable crying had nothing to do with her ability to mother him. He had slept all day to recover from the surgery. He was crying now because he'd urinated, and the urine was stinging his wound. I showed her how to diaper him and hold her baby so it wouldn't hurt his penis. I assured her that he would heal in a few days. I did everything to reassure her, especially about her mothering abilities. I helped quiet her baby, which calmed her down, too. Still, she wrote in her complaint that I had made her feel guilty for circumcising her baby. That, of course, was neither my intent nor my nature.

The next complaint came from a woman I had been expecting to meet who was going to give birth at Marin General Hospital. My friend Paul Tardiff told me he had given her information about circumcision and that she would not allow it. Paul had been circumcised as an adult and was willing to be interviewed by Dr. Dean Edell for the mini-documentary I had helped with. Paul said in his interview that the difference before and after circumcision was "like seeing in color and then seeing in black and white."

When I entered the new mother's room and she told me she was Paul's friend, I congratulated her on her decision to protect her son. Later, she mentioned my enthusiasm about her decision to one of the daytime nurses. The mother evidently was encouraged by the nurse to write a complaint about me, saying I might make someone feel guilty for circumcising their son. In all the years I've done this work, I have never lost that enthusiasm when a baby is spared. Yet, I once again found myself explaining that, as a mother of three circumcised boys, I would *never* say anything to make a mother feel guilty.

The third complaint came from a mother who did *not* want her second son circumcised. She said it was her husband who was insisting, just as he had with their first. When we first spoke, she was crying and wringing her hands. She went on to tell me all the reasons *not* to circumcise a baby. She was saying what I have said so many times—it's not medically necessary, it hurts, the trauma is undoubtedly lasting, and most importantly it is his body.

Of course, I agreed with her. I suggested she tell her husband that he made the decision for their first boy, so it was her turn to decide for this one. Clearly, she didn't have it in her to stand up to her husband. Instead, she complained that I had said all the accurate things she had actually said about the harm of circumcision. She blamed me for upsetting her. I had explained her dismay to her doctor when he arrived and said he needed to speak with her because she was so distraught. It was this doctor, I later learned, who was responsible for my being forced to resign from my job.

I was devastated by these mothers' complaints. I was learning firsthand the meaning of "kill the messenger." Probably this is the most difficult response for activists promoting an unfamiliar truth. I was also learning how a harmful practice can take hold in a culture. People raised within that culture will defend their cultural practice, even if it injures people they love, including their babies.

You cannot change another person's mind any more than you can make someone else happy. Whether circumcision, politics, weight loss, nutrition, or exercise, it is up to each individual to make up his or her own mind on a course of action based on access to the most accurate information.

I did not know what a hold cultural expectations about circumcision would have on both parents and healthcare professionals. At this point, my mission was to make sure that the information was clear, completely true, and available. Based on my own experience and my outreach, I knew people could learn—so I was not giving up.

Chapter 9

LIFE-ALTERING CHANGES

By 1985, my work at the hospital and my increasing role as an activist were consuming my time. Matt had always supported my work, but we were having other problems in our relationship, not for the first time, and struggling to communicate. Our conflicts at this point seemed insurmountable and I was feeling uncomfortable in my own home. I was glad my oldest three children with Joe were now adults in their 20s. I wasn't seeing much of Timothy, my son with Matt, who was 15 years old. Like most teenagers, he was interested in his friends, although on occasion he went on fun weekend outings with Matt.

With my marriage crumbling, I channeled all my personal energy into moving forward toward my goal. Sheila Curran and I filled out papers to set up a non-profit educational organization to be able to accept donations for spreading the message about circumcision versus an intact penis. Several other people in the country were working on the issue and we felt we could be more effective united under one umbrella.

One afternoon, Sheila and I sat down with Dean Edell to brainstorm names for our organization. Since circumcisions were called "circs" by doctors and nurses at the hospital, we decided on *Circumcision Information Resource Centers,* with the acronym CIRC. We were excited about the name, but I awoke in the middle of the night thinking, *our organization's acronym can't be CIRC; it has to be NOCIRC.* And that is how NOCIRC became a national organization.

In June 1985, the National Organization of Circumcision Information Resource Centers (NOCIRC) had its first booth at the Prenatal and Perinatal Psychology and Health Congress (PPPANA) in San Diego. When I left for the meeting, I took most of my clothes with me because I knew I did not want to go home to Forest Knolls.

To add to the concerns about my future and where I would live if my marriage was irretrievably broken, I learned about the third complaint against me while I was on my way to the conference. It was written by the woman who had herself explained to me why she did not want her son circumcised, but who then accused me of trying to coerce her. That was a low blow as it was apparent to me that I was a scapegoat for her inability to stand up to her husband, who wanted the circumcision. I knew I would be facing the potential termination of my employment at Marin General Hospital when I returned from the conference. What would I do for income and housing if I was going to live separately from Matt?

Thankfully, the Congress in San Diego was validating and energizing. As anthropologist and humanist Ashley Montagu stood at the podium to receive a prestigious Human Rights Award, he looked around the room and pointed to Sheila and me standing at our booth under the sign proclaiming our new organization:

National
Organization of
Circumcision
Information
Resource
Centers.

"I have been talking about the need to end circumcision for years," he said softly into the microphone. "And I'm glad to see someone has finally picked up the banner."

● ● ●

When I returned to Marin, I met with hospital administrators. My union representative was there to help me defend myself, but the writing was on the wall. I was stunned, afraid, and worried about my future. I had been speaking out about circumcision in the hospital long enough to know that nothing I said in my defense would make a difference—even if I was fulfilling my job description. I knew that the hospital administrators with whom I met had personal, cultural, religious, and/or financial interests and biases. I felt they had already made their decision.

I want to be clear, however, that it is nurses who are on the front lines when it comes to obtaining "informed consent" from patients—not doctors or administrators. *Legally*, this requires that the patient, guardian, or surrogate, is informed of the risks, benefits, and alternatives to a treatment, procedure, or surgery. A signature on the consent form provides legal documentation of consent. *Ethically*, consent is about *patient autonomy*, meaning the patient understands and freely agrees to the treatment. What administrators and physicians may not understand is that consent is a *process*, not a *form*.

My personal and professional position had always been that parents had the right to understand that they were signing a consent form for irreversible, medically unnecessary surgery. But I was also aware that circumcision was an emotionally and potentially volatile issue, and I never argued with a patient or staff member.

As the union representative walked me to my car after this fateful meeting at which I was "asked" to resign, he thanked me for having the courage to speak up in defense of baby boys. Grateful for his validation of my taking a stand on informed consent, and for being a patient advocate, I remembered this quote by Franklin Roosevelt: "Courage is not the absence of fear, but rather the assessment that something else is more important than fear."

I wondered which nurses at Marin General Hospital would have the courage now to tell mothers the truth about circumcision after I had been censored. Rather than my legacy at Marin General Hospital being one of protecting babies from unnecessary surgery by giving parents and healthcare workers the facts about circumcision, my efforts would now be a cautionary tale of how fulfilling my ethical and legal obligations as a nurse got me fired.

Someone needed to represent the baby who screamed his protest and anguish about what was being done to him—the amputation of the most sensitive part of his body without medical need, anesthesia, or his consent. The suffering of these infants was not being heard, recognized, or acknowledged.

The irony was that being forced to resign from Marin General liberated me to speak the truth and, along with Sheila, to finalize our papers for NOCIRC, the first non-profit national clearinghouse for accurate circumcision information in this or any other country. We didn't receive tax-exempt status until 1986, but we were already distributing information and our video, *Informed Consent,* as well as exhibiting at baby fairs. I was invited to speak at conferences, childbirth classes, men's groups, and on radio and television. Now I had no work schedule restricting my acceptance of these engagements. I was doing what I wanted to be doing: speaking the truth, educating parents, and protecting babies from unnecessary suffering.

A few years later, Ashley Montagu and I were having lunch in San Francisco. I told him I'd been forced to resign, i.e., *fired,* from my first job as a nurse. Ashley said, "I didn't realize you were fired, Marilyn. Congratulations, *you must have been doing something right!* And," he said with a grin, "you're in good company. I got fired from my first job, too!"

With that, this famous anthropologist and humanitarian offered me a new sense of pride and helped to alleviate the shame I felt for not being able to give people accurate information in a way that didn't offend them or make them defensive. I never doubted I was right in trying to educate parents and protect babies despite the overwhelming backlash bestowed upon the messenger. With this legendary man assuring and supporting me, I became even more confident and inspired.

Not long after my lunch with Ashley, Dr. Mitch Rider in Colorado sent me an article on social change. It said that society is like a herd of cattle and every cow in the herd must be turned if the herd is to take a new direction. Sometimes things happen that move a lot of the herd at one time. For example, with circumcision it could be the death of a baby or a million-dollar lawsuit following a botched circumcision that helped turn the herd, as well as the daily work of answering phone calls and letters. Handing information cards to pregnant women, staffing booths, and talking to groups of people whenever possible all contribute to bringing about a drop in circumcision rates. There was no way I could stop working toward my goal of educating every person in the U.S. and beyond.

The wisdom of those who preceded me in trying to change herd mentality sustained me, even as I continued to bemoan my situation and worry about how I would get funding for my work. Amazingly, validating both Mother Teresa and Goethe, money always arrived—often just a few days after voicing my anxious concerns, leaving me feeling silly for not "trusting totally." With time, I learned to keep my mouth shut and appreciate the help I received from people who supported the work I was doing.

● ● ●

I stayed at Sheila's place for a couple of weeks after returning from San Diego. I moved into her room at Dr. Jeff Anderson's home in Corte Madera, just north of San Francisco, where Jeff let me use a shed in his backyard for an office for my NOCIRC work. Even though Matt and I were not together, he kindly enclosed the shed to make it warmer for me during the fall and winter months. NOCIRC was reaching more people through radio, television, and newspaper articles. Our *Informed Consent* video was in high demand. Parents were becoming educated, and babies were being spared. But there was so much more to do.

I moved again when I learned that my friend Aneice Taylor needed a night attendant. Aneice was the mother of my son Timothy's classmate in the 1970s. We had become cartographers together. She and I were participating parents in the Open Classroom, and we took students hiking up and down the hills on one side of our valley to map trails used by animals and people. Developers had come into the valley to create a gated community. We were working to protect and preserve the natural beauty and habitat here in our valley in West Marin. At the end of the school year, the students presented our map to the San Geronimo Valley Planning Group, with a personal hand-written plea from elementary school student Lyza Sloan, asking for the preservation of our valley's natural beauty and the quality of our rural community. Thankfully, the gated community was never realized.

In 1982, a fierce storm had swept water and large trees down the hill behind Aneice's home in Lagunitas, the last village in our valley of four villages. The refrigerator was knocked over and landed on Aneice. She was blue when she was pulled from under it. Someone performed a tracheotomy so she could breathe, and she was taken to Marin General Hospital. The rest of the family was safe. I wasn't working that night because the flooding of the creek in our village was so severe, I couldn't cross the bridge to get onto the road out of the valley. A friend called the next day to tell me Aneice was in the intensive care unit and what had happened to her. During my shift the next night and every night for the rest of the week, I went to the ICU to help calm and comfort Aneice.

The most difficult moment for me was the first night in the hospital when Aneice told me she wanted to go home. I explained that she had been in a serious accident and needed to stay in the hospital until the doctors could determine exactly what had happened to her spine and how best to help her. She said, "Okay, Marilyn. If I promise not to leave, will you take the ropes off my arms and legs so I can move them?" I told her that there were no ropes and that's why the doctors needed to keep her in the hospital. Aneice's neck was broken at the level of her shoulders. She doesn't remember that conversation, but it is seared into my psyche and my heart.

I went to the Open Classroom the next morning and told the students I had been with Aneice all night at the hospital. I explained her condition after her accident. I told them she was on a special bed that helped to protect her spine and turn her from stomach to back without disturbing her body, especially her neck and spine. There was an opening—a "window" in the canvas—so when she was turned onto her stomach facing the floor she could breathe. I said that if they made paintings for Aneice, I would take them to the hospital so that she would have something to look at when she was facing down and looking through the "window." The nurses would change the drawings so Aneice could see them all. The large stack of paintings went with Aneice the following week when she was transferred to St. Mary's Hospital in San Francisco, which specializes in spinal cord injuries. The drawings and paintings hung on her hospital walls for the six months she was there.

Aneice's husband Gage bought another piece of property without large trees. He hired an architect and a foreman, and a wheelchair-friendly house was built by loving valley residents over the next eight months. All labor was donated. Everyone who worked on the house got lunch and a beer at the end of the day. When Aneice and her family finally moved in, we had a wonderful party, although it must have been very difficult for Aneice. She had been in the hospital for six months and had lived in a rental house until their new home was completed. Gage was already showing signs of not wanting to stay with his quadriplegic wife and two young children. He left them the following year.

Living with Aneice seemed like a good choice for both of us. I would be there if she needed help at night, and I would be free to do my NOCIRC work in the office shed during the day. It sounded perfect. I would be taking care of her needs until it was time to transfer her to bed at 11pm or so. I was usually in bed by 9pm, so this was a stretch for me, but I was happy to help. I also needed to get up at least once during the night to reposition Aneice. When I got her up in the morning, I took care of her personal needs until her daytime attendant arrived.

The most difficult part of my job was picking Aneice up out of her wheelchair to get her onto the bed at night and then getting her into the wheelchair in the morning. A few years later, Aneice switched from having one attendant for the week with weekend relief to two caregivers. She also got a lift that meant people no longer had to pick her up and put her into her wheelchair or onto the bed. That made it immensely easier for her caregivers.

During the year I lived with Aneice (1985/86), she realized that most quadriplegics in Marin County did not have enough money to pay for sufficient attendant care. Aneice had benefits from Aid to Families with Dependent Children, disability benefits, and Red Cross help, too, because she was a victim of a natural disaster. But there was a ceiling to the total amount of money she could receive from any agency. Her income was not sufficient to allow her to live at home. However, there was money enough for quadriplegics to live in institutions, where their quality of life is often poor, and their lives shortened because of it. Often those who chose to live at home but couldn't afford attendant care were left unattended in their wheelchair or on their bed for days at a time. So, Aneice founded a non-profit organization, InSpirit (In Support of Paralytics in Really Intense Times), to provide attendant care for paralytics. InSpirit could not provide financial support because of capped income regulations but it could pay for attendant care. It has helped paralytics for the past four decades.

Initially, Aneice used a mouth stick to type funding applications on her computer. Later, she was able to purchase a voice-activated computer. She worked every day to help quadriplegics experience a full life. I am honored to have been on the Board of Directors of InSpirit. Aneice demonstrated that, with help, quadriplegics can live at home, raise children, have meaningful lives, and be productive in their communities. She lived her life with grace, dignity, and a wonderful sense of humor. In 2020, Aneice died peacefully in her Woodacre home.

●●●

One weekend in 1985, Sheila and I drove to Los Angeles to meet with Dr. Paul Fleiss, a Los Angeles pediatrician who wanted to donate his Circumstraint to NOCIRC. The Circumstraint is a molded plastic board with four-point Velcro restraints to tether babies' arms and legs so they cannot move during the surgery. The baby's hips are elevated by the board to make the penis more accessible to the circumciser. When I worked at the hospital, I called the Circumstraint "the rack" because, to me, it was an instrument of torture. We've put an intact baby doll in it for our baby fair booth demonstrations. Dr. Fleiss had stopped doing circumcisions when he recognized the significance of the babies' screams. Until his death some 30 years later, he continued his advocacy to protect babies.

Sadly, on August 22, two infants suffered severe disfiguring electrical burns to the penis and adjacent areas when each of their physicians used an electric cauterizing needle as part of the circumcision procedure. According to an article in the *New York Times,*[26] the burns to one of the infants were so severe that his parents opted to surgically alter the sex of their son to a girl. The other parents honored their son's gender and raised him as a boy, following surgical repair. These were life-altering changes for the unfortunate families who had chosen circumcision for their baby boys in good faith that all would be well. I hurt for these people who, if they had left their sons' penises intact, could have avoided these tragedies. News of this kind—still happening today—is heartbreaking beyond comprehension.

The Atlanta hospital paid $22.8 million to the boy whose penis was burned off. He underwent several operations and continuous reconstructive surgeries were expected until he was 15 years old. He would never function sexually as a normal male and would require psychological counseling and lifelong urological care. The other circumcision case—the child who underwent a sex-change operation and was rendered incapable of reproduction—was also settled. The amount of the settlement was not disclosed. After these tragedies, the circumcision rate at Atlanta's Northside Hospital dropped dramatically. Unfortunately, with time, it rebounded, and the circumcision rate is again as high as it was before the horrific incidents occurred.

Meanwhile, helping Aneice at night and working all day, along with my increasing workload, was difficult. My natural rhythm is to rise early and go to bed early. I was becoming exhausted. Just as I wondered how I would be able to continue, Patty Craven, whose daughter's birth I had attended a few years earlier, donated $5,000 to NOCIRC. Thanks to her generosity, I found an office in San Anselmo that I could afford. With sadness, gratitude, and excitement, I resigned from my job with Aneice, moved my desk and some furniture into the front office, my couch into a very small back room, and put my NOCIRC sign in the window. That's where I worked and slept until August 1988.

With perfect timing, my daughter Kate and her son Matthew moved into Aneice's house to take care of her. I remember three-year-old Matthew climbing onto Aneice's lap and pointing where he wanted to go as she used her chin control to drive her wheelchair around the yard. They were adorable.

My sons were doing well. Timothy was living at home with Matt and going to school. Michael was working as a computer programmer in San Francisco. And Troy was inspired to go to New York to study dance and theater. I was grateful to be able to focus on the mission of NOCIRC and saving babies from the unnecessary risks of routine circumcision.

Chapter 10

PROGRESS AND OBSTACLES

In May 1986, the family of a young Louisiana boy was awarded $2.75 million by a jury after the boy's penis had to be amputated.[27] His penis had been irreparably damaged by an electrocautery instrument during a routine circumcision—the same thing that had happened to the two boys in Atlanta just nine months earlier. Once again, my heart ached for another boy who had suffered an unnecessary, preventable tragedy.

Following that successful legal case, the California Appellate Court judges heard the appeal in the Adam London lawsuit, originally filed by Richard Morris in 1984. The judges were asked the same question the lower court had been asked, "Do parents have a right to consent to a surgical procedure which has no medical purpose?" The judges asked about the parents' right to religious freedom. Morris, who stood behind a lectern facing the panel of judges sitting at a long table on a raised platform in front of him, was left to explain the obvious. "When marked as a Jew or Muslim by the absence of a foreskin and a scar on his penis, a child's right to freedom of religion has been violated and denied." Evidently the Appellate Court did not understand the simple explanation or the law behind it, nor did they protect the Constitutional right of the child to freedom of religion. Instead, the Court stamped on their ruling against the baby, *"Not for publication."* Were the judges ashamed of their finding? They certainly should have been.

The next appeal to this lawsuit was filed with the California Supreme Court, which refused to hear the case and stamped *Denied* on the cover of the brief. By this time, the court's inability to deal with the issue came as no surprise. I believe the judges simply lacked the moral courage to protect children's rights to bodily integrity, genital autonomy, and religious freedom. The laws of our country seemed clear; however, they are not applied to all citizens equally.

We didn't have enough money to appeal the case to the U.S. Supreme Court, which was just as well because those justices undoubtedly were not prepared to deal with our issue either. As my dear Lenny Bruce had said, "Justice is no better than the judges who sit on the bench."

Clearly, the rights of children in the United States of America are not ranked highly. Consider this: of the 193 countries recognized by the United Nations, the United States is the only country that has not ratified the *UN Convention on the Rights of the Child* (CRC). One would think this would be a no-brainer for a country that lays claim to one of the greatest human rights documents in history: the *Constitution of the United States* (albeit with 27 amendments). Yet our government and our courts have failed this basic moral test.

While the extensive media attention from our first circumcision lawsuit made the public aware of circumcision as an issue, it also alerted two San Francisco Bay Area physicians to the fact that routine infant circumcision was being challenged. Urologist Aaron Fink, whose own son had a botched circumcision on his eighth day of life, and Edgar Schoen, a pro-circumcision pediatrician at Kaiser Permanente, joined forces and began their efforts to give *medical* validity to cultural and religious circumcision by writing a pro-circumcision resolution that Fink introduced to the California Medical Association and Schoen took to the American Academy of Pediatrics in support of circumcision.

Schoen's rhyming poem, "Ode to the Circumcised Male," was published in the *American Journal of Diseases of Children.*[28] Considering lines like these, I can only question the sensitivity and sensibility of the editor who allowed this in a professional journal:

When you gaze through a looking glass, don't think of Alice;
don't rue that you suffered a rape of your phallus.
Just hope that one day you can say with a smile
that your glans ain't passe; it will rise up in style.

Knowing and hearing from men who felt they *had* suffered the rape of their phallus, which is not a laughing matter, I shudder to think of this flippant poem representing any physician's thinking. But it did then and still does now.

Schoen turned up as my opponent in many scenarios in my quest to end circumcision.

One of the most unusual documentaries I appeared in was the exposé of circumcision by Penn & Teller on their series *Bullshit!* on the Showtime network in 2005.[29] If you like their confrontational style, don't mind uncensored expletives, nudity, penis jokes, and are curious about seeing circumcision video footage, or a picture of female genital mutilation, you will learn something from this honest and provocative episode in which I appear fully clothed, although I speak the unembellished naked truth about circumcision. Their presentation of solid information may be unorthodox to those who have been reading scientific studies and magazine articles, but many parents have been educated and babies protected because of Penn & Teller's show. And—they gave the opposition a chance to make their case for circumcision, in particular my sparring partner Edgar Schoen, whom they also interviewed.

About this time, U.S. Army physician Thomas Wiswell published a paper in *Pediatrics* claiming that intact boys are more likely than circumcised boys to get urinary tract infections.[30] Wiswell based his conclusion on a statistical study he conducted of boys born in Army hospitals. He found that 1.12 percent of intact boys contracted a urinary tract infection (UTI) compared to 0.11 percent of circumcised boys, leading to his conclusion that "there is a ten-fold increase of UTI in uncircumcised boys." The use of "ten-fold" here is a typical example of how statistics are misrepresented to deceive the public. An increase from 1.00 to 1.12 percent still means that barely over one percent of intact boys will ever get a UTI. It also does nothing to convey the fact that urinary tract infections are easily treated with antibiotics in boys, just as they are in girls.

Wiswell was quoted in the *Boston Globe* a few years later, saying, "I have some good friends who are obstetricians outside the military, and they look at a foreskin and almost see a $125 price tag on it. Heck, if you do ten a week, that's over $1,000, and they don't take that much time."[31] What a crude way to express the value of the benefit of circumcision. But I'm sure some doctors and mohels do consider circumcision extra income. Today a mohel might be paid $500 to $1500, depending on their location in the U.S.

By autumn of 1986, the National Center for Health Statistics, a federal agency within the Department of Health and Human Services in Washington D.C. reported a decline in the number of hospital-performed circumcisions in the U.S. As more and more babies are kept intact, the "looking like everyone else in the locker room" excuse for circumcision has become less of a rationalization for parents to circumcise their boys.

After Dr. Dean Edell, Richard Steiner, and I appeared on the *AM San Francisco* television show in 1986 to discuss circumcision and foreskin reconstructive surgery (which Richard had undergone), we received an overwhelming number of requests for more information. Many men were dissatisfied with having been circumcised. Some had serious physical impairments that they were realizing had been caused by the surgery, and others reported problems with self-esteem due to a body alteration to which they had not consented. These themes continued to dominate the conversations I had with circumcised men decades after I first became an activist. I began my work to stop the screams of babies, and then men began to scream. They needed to be heard.

About the time of the *AM San Francisco Show,* I was contacted by Ed Wallerstein, who asked if I was willing to help a Jewish woman in Palo Alto, about two hours from where I live. She wanted to protect her baby but didn't want to hurt her parents by not having a bris or brit milah, the Jewish ritual symbolizing Abraham's contract with God. The mother-to-be contacted me at the same time a Jewish friend of mine with an intact teenage son was visiting. After I spoke with the woman and she explained why she was calling, I mentioned my visiting friend and said she would be happy to speak with her. They spoke for about a half hour and that was all it took.

It wasn't long before I was invited to attend a welcoming and naming ceremony for the baby in Palo Alto. One of the baby's parents was raised in an Orthodox Jewish community while the other was raised in a Conservative community. This would be a "New Brit Ceremony," and both sets of grandparents were present. The service began:

The Holy One, praised be He, said to our father Abraham, 'Walk thou before me and be thou perfect.' This child, created in your image, is whole, complete and perfect. We accept him as he has come to us and respect your creation by not changing it. He enters into Your Covenant. A new day has dawned.

The rabbi picked up his guitar instead of a scalpel and began singing, *To Life L'Chaim!* Everyone in the room was weeping, *except* the eight-day-old baby boy. He had been spared. This was the first Brit Shalom (Ceremony of Peace) I attended, and I felt blessed to have been part of the beautiful, non-violent ceremony.

●●●

On January 1, 1987, Blue Shield of Pennsylvania stopped paying for routine neonatal circumcision, calling it medically unnecessary. Blue Shield insurance plans in both California and Maine and Blue Cross of Washington/Alaska had already discontinued payment.

In March of that year, I learned that doctors Aaron Fink and Robert L. Bratman submitted their resolution to the California Medical Association, which, if passed, would qualify circumcision as an "effective public health measure" in the state. The CMA's Scientific Committee, headed at the time by Dr. Allen Mathies, Jr., heard a long list of reasons why circumcision is beneficial, but the Advisory Panel on Pediatrics and Urology recognized the flawed science and bias in the resolution and recommended that the "CMA *not* adopt Resolution 712-87." The resolution did not pass.

Writing in the April 1987 issue of the *American Journal of Public Health,* a group of military physicians reported that a case-controlled study of active-duty soldiers showed circumcised males are nearly twice as likely as intact males to contract non-gonococcal urethritis (NGU), a venereal disease that afflicts two million males each year. Based on these findings, they posited that "the prepuce (foreskin) has a protective effect against the acquisition of NGU."[32] This was significant because most Americans at the time believed that the foreskin had no purpose at all—a misconception that continues to plague the American debate about circumcision.

Scientific studies supported leaving males intact. The question was how to get that information to the public domain in a format that would be easily understood.

Chapter 11

NOCIRC TAKES THE MESSAGE TO NATIONAL TELEVISION

Something wonderful happened to help NOCIRC and its friends deliver the message to the public. I was contacted by a producer for the *Phil Donahue Show*, a live-audience television talk show based in New York City that ran on ABC from 1970 to 1996. The producer invited me to put together a panel of guests to speak on the issue of circumcision. They wanted someone who had had foreskin reconstruction surgery as well, so I suggested Richard Steiner who was willing to speak about the surgery he had undergone. I also suggested Trudie London who filed the first circumcision lawsuit on behalf of her son, and Dr. Dean Edell who was already speaking out against circumcision on his radio and television shows in San Francisco. His syndicated radio show was popular across the country.

When I mentioned my plan to go on *The Phil Donahue Show* to friends and colleagues, some cautioned me not to participate, calling it a potential "sex circus." But I knew that when people were given the correct information, they often recognized the harm of circumcision and changed their minds. I thought, if just one person hears me, if one baby is spared, it will be worth it. Given that the show aired in 214 outlets throughout the country, at least a lot of people would learn that circumcision was an important issue that needed to be discussed.[33]

Before I flew across the country to New York, I kept wondering how I would say what needed to be said. Babies were at stake here and the more I thought about it the more nervous and anxious I became.

Troy was living in New York at that time (June 1987), so he came to stay with me at the hotel to help calm my jitters. We called room service for dinner and talked until bedtime. At 4am the phone rang. Jeffrey Wood, of the organization INTACT, wanted to give me advice before the show, which wasn't for another 12 hours. He spent a long time telling me to speak slowly and not to stutter. Good advice, but something I've never been able to achieve. This early morning, well-meaning call made me even more nervous. I was awake for the day.

Hours later, a limousine came to take Dean, intactivist George Soule, Troy, and me to the studio. Just before the show, a woman came to greet us. She said, "You've come a long way to get your issue out. The first 20 minutes will be your chance to do that. After that, we open the discussion up to include the audience. During those first 20 minutes, talk fast, jump in, and don't worry about interrupting; it keeps everything lively."

"Wow!" They were telling me to do what I'd been told *not* to do my whole life. I remember thinking, "Okay! I *can* do this!"

On June 17, 1987, Dean Edell, Trudie London, Richard Steiner, and I appeared live on *The Donahue Show*.[34] Millions watched as Dean's mini-documentary footage showed a baby boy being circumcised. People heard the screams. The viewers and the audience heard us talk about the pain and harm of circumcision and the importance of protecting babies from that harm.

When the audience was included in the discussion, we saw the variations in people's reactions to our message. Some got defensive, bringing up all kinds of medical misinformation about a topic that was rarely if ever discussed or challenged. At the end of the show George Soule stood up in the audience and said: "From what we've learned today, it is obvious that circumcision is not practiced by most of the world, and it is not medically necessary. Since our doctors are promoting it, doesn't this make circumcision the largest medical scandal in U.S. history?"

We, of course, agreed.

There was no audience consensus. But Phil had given everyone on the panel, and those chosen from the audience, time to speak, and it was evident that he understood the issue and its emotional nature. For me, listening to the audience was eye-opening social research. I was amazed that even after watching a circumcision video and hearing the baby's screams, learning that circumcision is medically unnecessary, and that most of the world's males are intact, some people still were unwilling to recognize or accept these facts as truth.

When I flew home two days later, someone on the plane asked, "Didn't I just see you on *The Donahue Show*?" By the time the plane took off for California, everyone on the plane was talking about circumcision. I stopped at my post office on my way home and picked up 157 letters requesting information that had arrived since the show aired two days earlier. Over the next three weeks, more than 3000 letters arrived. That was the beginning. *The Phil Donahue Show* had put the issue of circumcision and NOCIRC on the map.

●●●

Following *The Donahue Show*, I was contacted by Ralph Ginzburg, a New York publisher who probably caused more controversy with small circulation periodicals than any other publisher in America. In 1962, Ginzburg published *Eros*, a quarterly that featured articles on the joys of love and sex and reprinted erotic works by such masters as Rembrandt, D. H. Lawrence, Picasso, Mark Twain, Michelangelo, Norman Mailer, Ovid, Ray Bradbury, and Shakespeare. The suppression of *Eros* by the United States Supreme Court, in one of its last major federal obscenity cases, led to Ginzburg's imprisonment ten years later, an experience he documented in his book, *Castrated: My Eight Months in Prison* (1973). On the day he was incarcerated, February 17, 1972, a full-page notice about the injustice of the prison sentence appeared in the *New York Times*, signed by hundreds of law professors, lawyers, ethicists, authors, and concerned individuals. It made me think about the censorship of Lenny Bruce.

Between his conviction in a lower court and incarceration, Ginzburg launched *Fact*, a magazine of dissent. The July-August 1966 issue featured an article by John M. Foley, "The Unkindest Cut of All."[35] In seeking to understand another doctor's call for compulsory circumcision, Foley wrote:

> *One answer, of course, is that if circumcision were made compulsory, the circumciser would be protected whenever he happens to cripple or kill the little boy he operates on—a complication that is not so very uncommon. Another answer, I think, must be sought in the darker regions of the human mind, because circumcision is simply an unmitigated fraud. It is nothing but wanton and unnecessary mutilation. The annual two million assembly line circumcisions in this country are a monument to the gullibility and stupidity of the American public.*

How I wish I had read that prior to the birth of my last son in 1969.

The reason Ginzburg contacted me was because in 1986 he had founded a nonprofit organization called OUCH (Outlaw Unnecessary Circumcision in Hospitals) to stop health insurance companies from funding circumcision surgery. Since he did not have the time to publicize OUCH, he wondered if I would speak for him. He hired a publicist to book me on radio and television shows nationwide and paid me for each interview and for my expenses. He used the $50,000 he invested in OUCH to pay for this purpose until the money was gone.

I was grateful for his generous help but was not surprised when the publicist, one of the best in the country, had a difficult time booking me. Disappointed, Ralph had not yet recognized the difficulty of the subject with which we were dealing or the resistance to our message. We were still in the early years of our movement and many people struggled with what we had to say while others defensively refused to believe us.

I knew Ralph was beginning to understand the difficulty of the topic when awhile later he said, "Marilyn, you're not going to end circumcision in your lifetime. It will never happen." I dismissed that remark in the moment, however, it nagged me throughout the day as I did my work. By the end of the day, Ralph's words came screaming back into my head, which I put down on my desk, sobbing. Finally exhausted, I blew my nose, wiped my face, and said out loud to only myself, "Well then, I'm going to die trying!"

Thankfully, the publicist did book me on radio and television shows across the country. These interviews continued for a couple of years before tapering off. I wondered why until someone sent me a quote attributed to Arthur Schopenhauer, who said: "All truth passes through three stages. First, it is ridiculed. Second, it is violently opposed. Third, it is accepted as being self-evident."

Shortly after that, I read an apt Gandhi quote about social change that inspired me: "First they ignore you, then they laugh at you, then they fight you, then you win." Later, I found out that what he actually said, documented in the book, *Freedom's Battle*, a collection of *Gandhi's* speeches, essays, and other writings first published in 1922, was "In a civilized country when ridicule fails to kill a movement it begins to command respect." This is where the movement to end medically unnecessary infant circumcision and grant equal rights to children is now, in 2023.

Due to my relentless pursuit of educating people about circumcision and making sure parents understood the informed consent they were given prior to agreeing to surgery on their newborn, I'd been impossible to ignore—initially, that is. Then, administrators silenced me at Marin General Hospital by forcing me to resign. At that time, Matt Milos said, "When they told Marilyn to keep her mouth shut, they told the *wrong* person!" I loved him for saying that and he loved that I could not be silenced—even after we were no longer living together.

I didn't care that I was considered a troublemaker because I had opened the door to discussion of a taboo subject—which was really penises and their foreskins rather than circumcision. In fact, the very existence of circumcision was an attempt to keep sexuality under wraps, going back to identifying circumcision as an antidote to masturbation, which was the cause of both physical diseases and mental disorders.

Talk show hosts invited me to interviews where I was often mocked, bullied, or ridiculed. What was I, a woman, doing talking about men's penises? When I responded with, "Before a man knows he has a penis to protect, a mother knows she has a baby to protect!" or any other reasonable response, hosts began arguing with me instead of laughing at me. I was experiencing what Schopenhauer and Gandhi said would happen: ridicule and opposition by uneducated bullies. Rather than internalizing scornful and taunting remarks, I relied on scientific knowledge, common sense, and gut wisdom for comebacks. I would not be silenced!

In 1988, Betty Katz Sperlich and Mary Conant, two nurses who worked at St. Vincent Hospital in Santa Fe, New Mexico, invited me to do an in-service at that hospital. I never had spoken formally to a group of nurses, doctors, and administrators but I had our *Informed Consent* and *Phil Donahue Show* videos to show them. I invited the attendees to watch audience reactions during the Donahue Show because they illustrated how people struggled with the issue

A few months later, I received the Maureen Ricke California Nurses Association Region 9's highest award for my "dedication and unwavering commitment to righting a wrong." To be honored by my peers was both thrilling and humbling, especially after being dismissed by Marin General Hospital for the work for which I was now receiving an award.

I appreciated the respect from my peers. And for a while, I was receiving requests for information from people who had been referred to NOCIRC by the American Academy of Pediatrics. However, as our influence was becoming more significant and the circumcision rate was declining, the AAP referrals to NOCIRC began to decline, too.

Even so, we continued to gain ground. The American Medical Association finally addressed the pain of circumcision. Howard J. Stang, MD, and colleagues at Group Health Inc., and the University of Minnesota reported: "There is no doubt that circumcisions are painful for the baby. Indeed, circumcision has become a model for the analysis of pain and stress responses in the newborn."[36] Recognizing that animals are anesthetized for surgeries, they asked, "[A]re we not morally obligated to do the same for the young of our human species?" It was after this article appeared in the *Journal of the American Medical Association* that anesthesia began to be used for circumcision. Today, decades later, many newborns continue to be circumcised without pain relief.

NOCIRC called upon the American Academy of Pediatrics (AAP) in a 26-page report that we mailed, citing dozens of medical studies, to strengthen its stand against circumcision. The report noted, "The U.S. is the only country in the world where the majority of infant boys are at risk for genital surgery without medical or religious reason." NOCIRC outlined five reasons to end newborn circumcision, including:

the protective functions of the foreskin,
the risks attending the surgery,
the pain inflicted on the baby,
the permanent scars of the operation, and
the ethical questions raised by unnecessary surgery on a non-consenting infant.

While we had hoped the AAP would consider our educated and accurate submission as it prepared its 1989 Task Force Committee on Circumcision Report, it did not. The Edgar Schoen-led AAP Task Force failed to recognize studies that found circumcision not only unnecessary but also destructive of the natural intact body. The AAP report fell short of protecting babies from unnecessary genital cutting or even supporting every doctor's oath to "First, do no harm."

Around this time, Jeffrey Wood shuttered his organization (INTACT) and began referring people to NOCIRC. In his announcement letter, he said, "NOCIRC has emerged as the foremost circumcision education group in the world today." I was grateful for the help and encouragement he offered me as I began my work.

●●●

A year and a half after our separation, Matt called to tell me he had been diagnosed with lymphoblastic lymphoma, a form of cancer that sounds as serious as it is. He came to my office to talk and, while there, picked up our family photo album. As we looked at the photos and talked about them, I thanked Matt for the many good times we had enjoyed during our 18 years together. We fell into each other's arms and wept. During the next 18 months, we had time to make our amends. I took part in Matt's end-of-life care at the home we had purchased together in Forest Knolls.

One day, lying on the couch with IV medications dripping into his veins, Matt's arms swayed in the air. He opened his eyes, looked at me, and said, "Didn't we dance well together?" I thought back to the parties we'd attended where we danced while our friends circled round, watched, and applauded when the dance ended.

"Yes," I said. "We did love dancing and others enjoyed our dancing, too!" Matt smiled.

We had danced in San Francisco, in Golden Gate Park, danced to the music of political revolution and freedom, danced with friends, with our children, in Mexico, across the country and around Marin County. We had danced in the light of the full moon and no moon. We had separated, but would always be connected, and I was grateful to be able to sway in rhythm by his bedside.

In August of 1988, a couple of weeks before he died, Matt talked to me about his burial. His thinking and memory were not clear because chemotherapy drugs had been put into his spinal fluid to kill the cancer in his brain. Clearly it had killed brain cells, too. I reminded Matt that he had already paid the Neptune Society to cremate his body, so he didn't need to worry about a burial site. Now we were getting to the reality of his demise. I looked at Matt with great sadness and said, "I'm going to miss you, Matt." As my eyes filled with tears, he patted me and said, "Don't cry, honey, don't cry. This is life." I asked him if he minded if I kept his last name. Milos means *love,* one of my first patients had told me. "Not personal love," he'd said, "but *universal love—agape*."

Matt said, "I would be honored if you keep my name." I'm grateful that we were able to find peace at the end of his life as we developed a new and deeper expression of the love we shared.

When I think about Matt now, it is with love for the man who shared 18 years with me, fathered one of my sons, and helped raise all my children. He calmed and mentored me when I was applying for and attending nursing school. He supported me in the early years of my work. We both did our best. Matt died gently in his sleep.

I moved from my office back into the Forest Knolls home we had bought 13 years earlier. Timothy, Kate, and her son Matthew continued living in the house, too. I made Matt's and my sun-filled bedroom into my office because it was the room where I began my work in 1979. It's still my office today.

BUILDING A SOCIAL MOVEMENT TO STOP CIRCUMCISION 1989–2018

Chapter 12

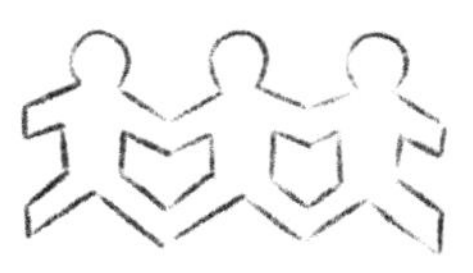

1ST INTERNATIONAL SYMPOSIUM ON CIRCUMCISION

New avenues for educating parents, the public, and healthcare professionals about the unnecessary pain and trauma of circumcision were opening. Requests for information from NOCIRC, and for my participation as a speaker in discussions about the issue of circumcision, were multiplying—and I responded to every lead.

I was grateful for the stability of the home where Matt and I had lived as I was working 12 to 15 hours a day, seven days a week. I finally had a solid list of contacts for outreach and was interacting with brilliant minds. But I could almost feel the whoosh of time as it zoomed by. Doing everything I could every single day wasn't enough when physicians and organizations continued to endorse newborn circumcision as an effective public health measure despite evidence to the contrary. Hurting healthy infants with non-therapeutic, potentially dangerous, and thus indefensible, surgery was mind-boggling. It had to be stopped!

I kept asking myself this: *What prompts physicians and their organizations, as well as state governments, past and present, to ignore the truth about circumcision and defend the status quo?* What's at stake must be more than money.

I kept going back to the history of circumcision presented in Ed Wallerstein's book. His research revealed that the reasons for circumcision in the nineteenth and early twentieth centuries were based on false beliefs about how the body and mind worked, as well as on stigmas and prejudices, and skewed studies based on particular populations—often poor, rural, and minorities. But we knew by the 1980s that circumcision did not prevent masturbation or sexual desire. An entire country of mostly circumcised males did not prevent the sexual revolution of the 1960s and 1970s. We also knew about infections and germs and that circumcision did not prevent STDs. We knew, or could be taught, that hygiene of an intact penis is simple.

I was learning again and again that proponents of circumcision, whether medically trained physicians or clueless administrators have complicated motives. But the most insidious of these motives for circumcision were based on myths, prejudice, and avarice. Even though most of the world's males were intact and as likely to be successful and healthy as their circumcised peers, an intact foreskin in the United States was still associated with disease and poverty and considered less attractive than a denuded glans.

In the 10 years since my awakening to the brutality of infant circumcision in 1979, I had been attacked for my commitment to ending circumcision as if I were an out-of-control hysterical woman trying to insert myself into men's business. I had been dismissed from a job I loved for sharing honest, accurate information with new moms about circumcision before they signed the consent form—a task I was legally and ethically obliged to fulfill.

At least by now I knew I was not alone in my efforts. NOCIRC had a ripple effect as it touched people, mainly in the San Francisco Bay Area, and then around the country with *The Phil Donahue Show*. I was beginning to feel there was a wave building up that would carry the message beyond my singular capacity. By 1988, rates of circumcision in newborns in the hospital had decreased in the U.S. from a high of 65 percent in 1981 to 58 percent.[37]

Something was happening.

In 1988, Drs. Fink and Bratman submitted another resolution in favor of newborn circumcision to the California Medical Association. The issue was again presented and discussed in committee hearings and on the floor of the convention. Urologist Arthur Dick (I kid you not) circumcised a banana to seal the deal before 442 delegates voted to adopt the resolution.

Months later I received a letter from John W. Hardebeck, MD, who had submitted a resolution to the California Medical Association requesting that the CMA withdraw its endorsement of newborn circumcision as an effective public health measure; further it requested that the CMA state that newborn circumcision is mostly unnecessary and contraindicated, and wherever done should be accompanied by a parents' informational brochure or video and an informed consent form. This was a welcome step in the right direction.

When John asked if I knew anyone who would testify in support of his resolution, I told him urologist James Snyder, the first doctor to support my efforts, would be perfect.

At about the same time, the American Academy of Pediatrics had established a Task Force on Circumcision headed by Fink's pro-circumcision buddy pediatrician Edgar Schoen. With both the CMA and the AAP staged to present a case for circumcision, Donna Macris, a Certified Nurse-Midwife from Fresno, Sheila Curran, and I decided to organize the 1st International Symposium on Circumcision to counter their efforts.[38]

For the first time in history, we would invite scholars from religious, anthropological, sociological, medical, psychological, and legal disciplines to gather to discuss circumcision from their expert perspectives. NOCIRC had enough credibility at that point that I was able to put together a great roster of speakers whose papers on circumcision I had read during the first decade of my work.

I boldly invited French physician, author, childbirth expert, and founder of the Primal Health Medical Centre in London, Dr. Michel Odent, to speak because he had spent his life challenging the conventions of medical orthodoxy. Dr. Odent understood how birth and what we do to babies at the beginning of life have lifetime consequences. When he asked if there were other international speakers at our international symposium, I confessed there were not. Without hesitation, he said, "Well then, you need me." I certainly did. Dr. Odent provided us with a wonderful start and spoke at other symposia over the years.

We held the 1st International Symposium on Circumcision at the Emerald Hotel in Anaheim, California, March 1-3, 1989, across the street from the Disneyland Hotel where the California Medical Association was hosting its annual convention the day after our symposium ended. I knew the fees charged for attendees would not cover all the expenses of the event. Funds from NOCIRC and its donors were used to make up the shortfall since this was an essential investment in the quest to end circumcision.

I was, perhaps, the only person who was happy about a fire alarm that awakened everyone in the hotel to march outside and wait until the fire department determined it was a false alarm. To make up for the inconvenience, the hotel not only gave our group its breakfast buffet for free, but added some extras, which curtailed some of our expenses—a small blessing.

My goal for the event was to foster a reasonable discussion about how we came to accept cutting off normal genital parts of infants and children and what we could do to bring this anachronistic blood ritual to an end. I didn't want the symposium to "preach to the choir," which wouldn't change anyone's mind. To that end, I invited circumcision proponents Edgar Schoen and Aaron Fink to speak, as well as speakers who wanted to end circumcision. They did not respond to my invitation.

The physicians, psychologists, biblical and medical historians, and attorneys who participated gave remarkable presentations. Howard Stang, MD, promoter of the penile dorsal nerve block, who later went on to design a "softer" circumcision restraint, spoke about relieving the pain of circumcision. That's easily done without any special effort, but, I thought—*just stop circumcising babies!* That is not what he suggested, but his viewpoint was noted and appreciated even if it did not reflect my solution. At least he cared about and acknowledged the pain that infants do, in fact, feel—a victory of sorts.

Joel Schulson, a mohel I'd met when we were radio talk show guests in Philadelphia, exposed his ignorance about a normal body's reaction to trauma when he described pulling a baby's foreskin back prior to circumcising him and revealing the "putrid" substance underneath. In truth, prematurely retracting a newborn's foreskin tears it from the glans (head of the penis) so that blood, lymph with its protective white blood cells, and cells that have been damaged are sloughed following the trauma. Clearly, this circumciser did not understand the human body nor its normal reaction to physical trauma. That made me squirm and fume internally, but he had his say.

Fran Hosken, author of *The Hosken Report: Genital and Sexual Mutilations of Females* and the founder of Women's International Network News, overwhelmed attendees with her film that showed a young girl undergoing genital cutting. This was also a pressing issue that deserved consideration and widespread exposure.

A sobering talk by urologist James Snyder began with accounts of several serious circumcision accidents he had treated. Jim emphasized that these are only the tip of the iceberg because such events are so sensitive and confidential they had not yet been seriously studied in the medical literature. He also pointed out that in the 1960s medical students were told that circumcision was a means of preventing cancer of the cervix. But by 1989 evidence showed that cervical cancer can be caused by multiple factors, including early onset of sexual activity, multiple sexual partners, sexually transmitted viruses, and other events and exposures unrelated to circumcision. Unfortunately, to this day some health professionals continue to advocate for circumcision as cancer prevention, and many parents today still believe the myth.

The same lack of up-to-date knowledge by medical practitioners applies to the idea that circumcision prevents urinary tract infections (UTIs) in infants. Jim cited documentation showing that more than 95 percent of male children do not get UTIs, and that in both girls and boys, a UTI can be easily treated with an inexpensive antibiotic, as opposed to prophylactic surgery. *Why is this easy-to-disprove myth still being treated as fact?*

Perhaps most disturbing, according to Jim, was the idea that circumcision can prevent HIV. First linked with promiscuity in homosexual males, and later with infected blood transfusions and sharing of needles among intravenous drug users, it should have been obvious that circumcision offered no protection from AIDS, given that most American males were already circumcised when the AIDS epidemic began in the United States in the 1980s. While there are now viable drugs to treat HIV, in 1989 safe sex or abstinence were the only reliable ways to prevent HIV infection and AIDS.

The three-day event had a profound effect on speakers and participants alike. Writing this, more than 40 years after I witnessed that first circumcision, I am still shocked by the violence to the child and the entitlement of the adults who permit this violence, as well as by the lack of any scientific basis for the benefits of circumcision. It was, and is, dumbfounding.

Each evening during the symposium, a group of us met in the hotel room that midwife Donna and nurses Sheila, Diane Stephens, and I shared to work on a Declaration of the 1st International Symposium on Circumcision. In it, we affirmed the basic human right of all human beings to an intact body and declared that parents, physicians, and other healthcare providers have a responsibility to refuse to remove or mutilate normal parts of the body. We also opposed any further medical studies that involved circumcising non-consenting minors and called on healthcare providers to teach hygiene and care of the intact penis. Our intention was to place the medical community on notice that it is being held accountable for misconstruing the scientific database available on human circumcision in the world at that time. Committing our beliefs to this document served as a guiding light for future symposia and goals I would return to throughout my struggle to end infant and child circumcision.

Chapter 13

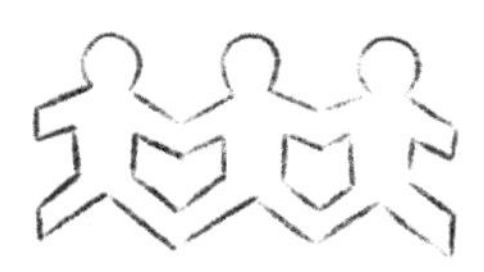

CHALLENGING THE MEDICAL ESTABLISHMENT

The day after our symposium, I walked across the street with Jim Snyder to where the California Medical Association (CMA) convention was being held. We took a seat on "our" side of the aisle, with Aaron Fink and his colleagues on the other side, reminding me of dueling political parties in our U.S. Congress. Committee members took their seats on the platform, looming above us.

When his name was called, Dr. John Hardebeck strolled up to the microphone and said, "I am the author of the resolution requesting that the CMA withdraw its endorsement of newborn circumcision as an effective public health measure, and I'm the head of IPC, Intact Physicians of California. Before today, I thought I was the only uncircumcised physician, but after hanging out in the men's room this morning, I discovered there are more of us than I realized."

Laughter broke out. John had managed to humanize the divide between those lined up on different sides of the aisle. I turned to see Fink's face. He was obviously struggling to maintain a dour expression in response to John's light-hearted humor that other attendees were enjoying.

When it was Jim's turn to speak in support of John's resolution, his testimony was the most eloquent and compelling of all the supporting speakers. He documented the tragic cases he had spoken about at NOCIRC's symposium—one causing death and others resulting in loss of normal penis function, or the entire penis. It was horrific.

Sadly, Hardebeck's challenge to the CMA's endorsement of circumcision was voted down. Even today, I have no words to express this perversion of justice. I cannot imagine a stronger, more urgent plea for reconsideration than the evidence Jim presented.

What would it take for a medical organization to admit it was wrong? Or was it just the specific people who represented the organization who were determined to maintain the status quo of blind ignorance in the face of facts?

Arriving home on Sunday evening after the excitement of the first symposium, and the drama and disappointment of the CMA meeting, I had no time to savor or process the events of the preceding week. The phone began ringing early Monday morning with reporters asking me for a comment about the just-released American Academy of Pediatrics' 1989 AAP Task Force Committee's Position Paper on Circumcision.

The report produced by Edgar Schoen's committee said there were benefits to circumcision as well as risks. What it failed to say is that *the known risks outweigh the potential benefits of circumcision*. Nor did it say anything about the structures, functions, development, and care of the normal penis, the pain and trauma inflicted on infants by circumcision, the harm of pain and trauma to the developing brain, or the right of the child to his normal body. In other words, the report was biased and therefore useless. This was business as usual, maintaining the status quo. *Why even convene a task force committee if it does not reflect current documentation?*

I later learned that Schoen proposed Fink's CMA endorsement of circumcision as the starting point for the Task Force committee. He was debated by one informed doctor on the Task Force who recognized

Schoen's strategy to railroad a pro-circumcision resolution through the American Academy of Pediatrics (AAP) Task Force committee. So, in the end, the responsibility for being informed about the benefits and risks of circumcision falls to prospective parents. At least they had NOCIRC, which would distribute accurate information. But we were not reaching every parent in the country. It was my hope that we would, but at that point we did not have the audience or presumed "authority" that the AAP had.

● ● ●

My heart was heavy because Jim Snyder's plea in support of John Hardebeck's corrective resolution to the CMA fell on deaf ears. And I was disappointed that the AAP's circumcision statement lacked essential information. Yet, buoyed by the good energy of the symposium, I knew I wanted to continue bringing experts together to share information and to give context to the various issues surrounding circumcision. I didn't know how, but it was going to happen.

Shortly after the AAP's 1989 announcement, *Prisoners of Ritual: An Odyssey into Female Circumcision in Africa*, written by independent researcher Hanny Lightfoot-Klein, was published. I contacted Hanny because, while she focused on the issue of female genital mutilation, she also addressed male circumcision and seemed friendly to our cause. When I was in New York City for a radio interview at the same time Hanny was there on business, Hanny generously introduced me to a supporter of her work who would become NOCIRC's benefactor for the next 12 years: Laurance Rockefeller.

Waiting for our meeting, I was surprised by the simplicity of the lobby of the Rockefeller family offices at the Art Deco inspired 30

Rockefeller Plaza and awed by the view from the large windows. When we were called into Laurance's office, the tall, soft-spoken gentleman asked about my founding of NOCIRC, my symposium, and my plans for the future, which included more symposia. After our meeting, Laurance donated $20,000 to support NOCIRC's efforts. That was the money I needed to "take this show on the road."

Chapter 14

2ND SYMPOSIUM AND A NEW RELATIONSHIP

With the help of Laurance Rockefeller's generous donation, I hired a company certified to offer continuing medical education credits for physicians to help organize our second symposium. I hoped offering credits that doctors must acquire to stay licensed would be an incentive for them to attend. I bought mailing lists with addresses of obstetricians, pediatricians, and urologists on the West Coast, East Coast, and in Illinois (where the AAP headquarters is located) and sent out 85,000 fliers to promote our symposium.

While Donna, the midwife, and I were preparing the Syllabus of Abstracts for this symposium, we went to dinner at a local café. Because it was so crowded, we were seated at one end of a table while another couple sat at the other end. We had taken our work with us and, as we began sorting through papers, the man sitting across from us appeared interested and asked if we were writing a book. I told him we were working on a program for a human rights symposium, not wanting to bring the "c" word to strangers at the dinner table.

He asked what the topic was, so I told him it was a children's rights issue. Again, he wanted to know more, so I told him the symposium was about circumcision. When he said he was Jewish, I responded by saying I thought that perhaps Jewish men had less circumcision trauma because they were part of a community that celebrates the ritual, so the trauma didn't remain hidden in the psyche.

He said, "You're wrong," and told me that during primal therapy he had relived his circumcision. His mother had handed him over to his grandfather who held him down while his whole family watched the mohel cut off the most sensitive part of his body. "No one stopped him, no one protected me from the pain, and no one responded to my screams," he said. "It was the most terrifying moment of my life, and I have had trust issues ever since." Since then, I have heard similarly disturbing stories from many circumcised men.

Donna and I wanted to present Dr. Benjamin Spock with the first Human Rights Award of the International Symposia on Circumcision for having the courage to change his mind about circumcision. Dr. Spock was an American pediatrician and liberal political activist whose book, *Baby and Childcare,* sold 500,000 copies in the six months following its publication in 1946, and 50 million by the time of his death in 1998. His first book promoted circumcision for the medical reasons that were given for doing it post-WWII in the U.S. Years later, he said, "My own preference, if I had the good fortune to have another son, would be to leave his little penis alone."[39]

Since he was unable to attend the symposium to accept his award, we met Dr. Spock at the Monterey Aquarium, where he loved watching the otters feed. A cameraman videotaped the event for us to show at the symposium. At lunch that day, Dr. Spock had said, "It's not easy to change your mind, Marilyn. When you do, a lot of people get mad at you." I understood that from my own experience.

Nearly 200 people attended NOCIRC's 2nd International Symposium on Circumcision, held at the Miyako Hotel in San Francisco,

April 30-May 3, 1991. Both anthropologist Ashley Montagu, who gave the keynote address, and Michel Odent, who closed the symposium, acknowledged our international symposia as the *crux of the human rights movement.* They emphasized the importance of accepting every new human being into the world with respect, dignity, compassion, and love—and recognized that acts of violence against newborns and children have a shattering effect upon all of humanity.

More urologists, nurses, midwives, and other concerned individuals attended the symposium than those who perform most circumcisions—obstetricians and pediatricians. *Why was that?*

Did circumcisers not come because they never see the untoward consequences of their handiwork when things go wrong? They *must* hear or read about cases where a baby was irreversibly damaged, and a doctor was sued. Or did they sometimes see the immediate consequences of this medically unnecessary surgery on an infant, feel some burden of guilt, and then become too defensive to listen to other viewpoints? Did it have to do with money? Power? Fear of opposing the status quo? Or all these things?

If doctors were unwilling to even discuss problems related to performing non-therapeutic circumcision on infants and children, then I needed to appeal to lawyers—who could, and hopefully would, defend the rights of those infants and children.

● ● ●

Paul Tardiff, who had appeared in Dean Edell's mini-documentary a decade earlier, helped Donna, Sheila, and me coordinate the second symposium but was unable to attend because he was seriously ill. After the symposium, Donna and I visited Paul at the hospital to tell him about how successful and inspiring it had been. He shed a tear of joy and satisfaction, passing a few days later. Paul's support continued, however, through the kind donation of his Ford Bronco to NOCIRC, which I plastered with bumper stickers people had sent me: e.g., "We are helping STOP routine circumcision," "www.nocirc.org," and the "Skins Bandwagon." Remember, this was before widespread use of the Internet. We got the word out any way we could. We dubbed the car the "NOCIRC-mobile."

In late January 1992, when the vehicle did not slow down in second gear as I was going downhill, I took it to a shop to have it fixed. The mechanic looked at the bumper stickers and read the license plate out loud, "NOCIRC 1." As soon as I began to tell him about the work I was doing, he said, "Well, shouldn't the decision be up to the person who owns the foreskin?" Wow, that was easy, I thought. He was clearly a friend, not foe.

While taking the car for a test drive with me, the mechanic, Ken Brierley, suddenly stopped the car in the middle of the street. I was momentarily quiet but when he began to drive again, I continued talking about my work. This happened twice more. The third time, he said, "Okay, now I need you to pray." I asked why and he said, "Because I need to listen to your car so I can figure out what's wrong with it." Aha! That was one of the more clever ways of getting me to shut up (and believe me many have tried). I laughed and stopped talking so he could focus on what the car was saying to him.

I ended up leaving my car for a couple of days so Ken could rebuild the transmission. After I picked it up and was driving home in the rain, one of the headlights went out. I called Ken the next morning and he said to stop in so he could fix the light. He refused to charge me for the repair.

A few days later I attempted to drive my car from my parking spot across the street from my house. The wheels began to spin out in the mud and the rear end began to slide toward the bank of the creek with its steep drop. Afraid to try further, I called a tow truck. The driver attached hooks and chains to the car and jolted it sideways into the street. I parked my car safely in my driveway.

The next day, the Bronco started making a troubling new noise. I immediately called Ken since he was the last person to work on the car. After checking the car, Ken said it was the brakes, which the tow truck had damaged, that were causing the sound. Ken took me to the specialty garage next door to his shop and they agreed to fix the problem. Again, Ken didn't charge me.

I told Ken I wanted to do something for him for being so helpful and not charging me for his work. Since I am a certified massage therapist, I asked if he would like a massage—probably one of the more unusual offers he had received to repay him for his mechanic's skills and generosity.

He considered the idea and scheduled a massage, which I did out of my home. Afterwards, he stayed, and we talked and talked.

A few days later when I went to pick up my car at the garage, Ken saw me walk past the open doors of his shop. He came out to tell me he'd been hiking the previous day and wondered if he could come for another massage. He came that evening and again stayed after the massage and again we spent hours talking. Ken told me his birthday was the following Friday. On Friday morning I called the automotive shop and invited him to dinner if he had no plans. Our first date was at a Mexican restaurant in Mill Valley.

Ken and I had been dating for a couple of months when he asked for a copy of *The TruthSeeker* magazine, which contained the proceedings of our first symposium. Shortly after that, he told his nine- and 11-year-old daughters about me and showed them the photo of me from the magazine, which was from a professional photo shoot years ago.

A couple of weeks after I'd met Ken's daughters, we took them to the nearby schoolyard to roller skate on the freshly laid blacktop. When I sat down on a bench to tighten my laces, Crystal, the younger daughter, sat down beside me. She was quiet for a moment and then said, "You look *fine,* but you looked so *pretty* in the picture."

It took some effort not to laugh! No sooner had Crystal and I gotten back to skating than her sister, Donelle, skated up and asked me, "Just how old are you anyway?" Ken had mentioned I was older than him. She wanted to know by exactly how much! We still laugh about their comments and the honesty of children. Once Ken and I realized there were 18 years between us, we decided that since I was younger than his mother and he was older than my children, we were in the same ballpark. We have now been together for 30 years.

Chapter 15

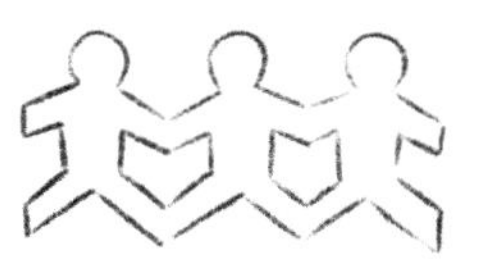

NURSES LEAD THE WAY

In the Spring of 1993, Ken and I drove to Santa Fe for a conference at St. Vincent Hospital where nurses had hit upon an unusual stance regarding their position on circumcision. In October 1986, four nurses working in the newborn nursery at St. Vincent submitted a letter to the nurse manager stating that they no longer wanted to assist with routine circumcision of newborns on ethical grounds. They had come to this conclusion for various reasons. For Mary Conant, it was "the sheer torture of it."[40] Her colleague, Betty Katz Sperlich, "seemed to have understood instantly with the first circumcision she witnessed that something was horribly wrong."[41] The response to their letter was that they would not be excused from participating in circumcisions.

Like me, they immediately began educating themselves and others and came to the same conclusion—that cutting off part of a baby's normal anatomy was a human rights as well as a medical issue. We were on the same journey, following similar paths. Prior to their letter, they had spent six years working for change within the system. They only decided to declare themselves conscientious objectors to circumcision when all other avenues to their non-participation were exhausted.[42]

To the surprise of the original four nurses, 20 more—about half the maternity unit nursing staff at St. Vincent Hospital, including all the unit's Jewish nurses—signed the letter citing circumcision as a violation of human rights. Their reasons for refusing to assist with infant circumcision included the violation of the baby's right to an intact body and lack of any compelling medical reasons for the pain and risks. In addition, they stated that printed parental information for informed consent was incomplete and parents were not properly informed of the dangers of the surgery, which included the possibility of "bleeding, infection, mutilation, and even death," which is what I had said in my revision of parental consent forms for Marin General Hospital.

This was the first time in the United States that a group of nurses had refused to assist with the surgery. You can imagine my gratitude and compassion for these nurses for coming forward and speaking out. As I knew too well, they could all lose their jobs. The conference I attended on May 8, 1993, was an opportunity to highlight the issue.

Apparently mindful of presenting a balanced program, the organizers had invited Dr. Thomas Wiswell to speak as a circumcision advocate. Dr. Martin Altshul, whose research had refuted Wiswell's work, was also invited to speak about his research, and then I spoke, honoring women's instincts to love and protect their babies.

During the question-and-answer session, Ken asked Dr. Wiswell if he thought the foreskin was a mistake of nature. Wiswell answered, "Yes, it is."

Either Wiswell knew nothing about the important protective, immunological, sensual, and sexual functions of the foreskin or he did and didn't want to admit he knew the harm of circumcision. I won't even get into the entitlement and grandiosity a man must feel to proclaim a normal and natural part of the penis "a mistake of nature." I held my tongue. My presentation conveyed my stance.

Following the event, speakers were invited to a reception. After several glasses of wine and a bowl of cherries, Dr. Wiswell admitted he knew his urinary tract infection studies were flawed. Even so, that never stopped him from touting them in his advocacy for circumcision. I thought of the doctor telling me, "**There is no medical reason for this**" after the circumcision I witnessed 15 years earlier when I was in nursing school.

To fast forward, in January 1995, St. Vincent Hospital and the local chapter of the National Union of Hospital and Health Care Employees reached an agreement, and a document called a "Memo of Understanding" was created. Although hospital officials did not institute a special consent form, claiming it would be too difficult to implement, they did grant the nurses the legal right, as conscientious objectors, to refuse to participate in newborn circumcisions.

One by one, doctors at St. Vincent Hospital stopped doing circumcisions. As they did, the nurses took each one a beautiful orchid plant.

The activism of the St. Vincent maternity unit nurses contributed to a dramatic decline of circumcisions at the hospital. In 2001, the circumcision rate at St. Vincent's was one of the lowest in the U.S., at 4 percent.[43]

Over time, the original conscientious objector nurses moved on from their jobs at the hospital, and in 2008 St. Vincent Hospital was sold. The new hospital administration and their doctors went back to circumcising babies. Hopefully, one day, nurses there and everywhere will again recognize the need—and have the courage—to take a conscientious objector stand against non-therapeutic circumcision. They have amazing role models to follow.

Chapter 16

LOSING MY MOTHER AND MY BROTHER

The morning after the 1993 St. Vincent conference was Mother's Day. We had breakfast with some of the nurses at our bed and breakfast and discussed the success of their event. After breakfast and saying our farewells, I called my mother to wish her a happy day. I was shocked and sad to hear that she had just been diagnosed with terminal cancer and was given four to eight weeks to live.

Ken and I had planned a leisurely trip home, during which we would stop off at local hospitals from New Mexico to California to provide them with circumcision information and patient handouts. We drove from Santa Fe to Taos and found a sweet little room in a motel, where I broke down and mourned the impending loss of my mother.

From there, we camped on the north rim of the Grand Canyon, our first experience at this magnificent place. The view of the canyon itself, the smell of the trees, and the sparsely inhabited campground were all welcoming. As the clouds formed and the hail began to fall, Ken and I quickly understood why we were the only campers in a tent. White, icy nuggets pounded the ground, only to melt sometime after midnight and form a river that made its way through our tent and sleeping bags by the wee hours of the morning.

And then we hurried home, making a couple of quick stops to drop off NOCIRC information at hospitals along the way. We would pull into the parking lot, I would change out of my comfortable pants, put on panty hose and a skirt, and take information packets to the nurses who worked in the hospital. I hoped our efforts planted a seed.

We took care of what needed to be done once we got home and packed up again, this time with my grandson Matthew. We drove to my brother Court's historical landmark home in Portland, Oregon, a bed and breakfast called Mumford Manor that my brother's wife managed, and where my mother would live out the rest of her life. (Court had brought my mother to Portland for a doctor's evaluation while I was in New Mexico.) Thankfully, the Manor could easily accommodate all my family who were coming to say goodbye to Grandma. We settled in.

That first night we were all gathered in my mother's room, where she was sitting up in bed as we talked. She listened to the din for a few minutes and then clapped her hands and said, "You are all talking to each other and not me—the one who is dying here. Where's the attention I'm s'posed to be getting?" We laughed. She knew, without a doubt, she was loved. Everyone stayed for a couple of days, said their farewells individually, and then headed home. Once I had settled into a routine with my mother, Ken and Matthew drove home, too.

My mother had helped support me in the early years of my work simply because I was her daughter. But after I left Marin General Hospital, she asked again and again why I didn't go back to work at another hospital so I could make a decent living. I told her that, although I loved nursing, I was driven by a higher calling to help end routine infant circumcision. She didn't understand my passion, but she listened and didn't argue the point.

As she lay on her deathbed, the *Marin Independent Journal*, a local newspaper, published an article about my work.[44] Years earlier, Dr. Dean Edell had sent the writer of the article to me for circumcision information. Once informed, she had eagerly protected her son when he was born. Now, at 12 or 13, a doctor had (mis)diagnosed her son with phimosis, a non-retractile foreskin, which is normal in infancy, childhood, and sometimes until the mid-twenties. The average age for foreskin retractability is 10.4 years and her son was well within normal developmental limits. He was not having problems and he did not need a circumcision. I told his mother, "You protected him once and now it's time to protect him again." She did, and then she wrote her newspaper article.

In her article, Dean Edell, who was my mother's favorite radio talk-show host and her hero, was quoted as saying, "We've all heard about outstanding people who make a difference in the world, but we rarely get to meet someone who has. Marilyn is one of those people. She's the real deal!"

My mother asked me to read that quote to her about a dozen times. Not only did Dean give me credibility, but he also helped my mother feel that supporting my work was a worthwhile thing to have done. His comment was a gift to us both.

As my mother drew closer to death, she looked more relaxed and at ease than I had ever seen her. That's not how she'd been when I first arrived at Court's house in Portland. She was overdosed on pain medication and extremely fearful. Once I had her medications adjusted, her paranoia disappeared. She was comfortable then. Knowing she had just weeks to live, she'd gotten right to the business of dying. She wavered between wakeful moments and a light, drug-enhanced sleep.

A day or two before she died, my mother awoke from a nap. As she opened her eyes, she asked, "Am I still here?"

"Yes, Mom," I said, "you're still here."

She surprised me when she said, "*Oh shit!*" I'd only heard her curse once when she said "damn" under her breath when I was about 12 years old. I knew she wanted this transition to be over, to be on her way to whatever was to come next.

To give her something to think about and hopefully look forward to, I asked, "Who do you think is going to meet you on the other side? Do you think it will be Grandmommy?" (her mother).

"Oh no," she answered, "she didn't believe in an afterlife. It won't be her!"

"Maybe it will be Granddaddy," I suggested.

My mother immediately answered, "Oh no! I don't want him there!"

With that, I had a sudden realization, one that took me back to my own early childhood. My brother and I had been left with our maternal grandparents for a week when our parents went on a vacation. My grandfather did lots of things with me—he taught me how to play checkers, shoot a BB gun and a rifle, and helped me build a go-cart. Then, one day in his garage, he put his large hand into my panties and touched my tender little girl parts with his large sandpaper-rough fingers. This happened on two occasions that I can remember. I've tried unsuccessfully to access additional memories from that time, or times before this visit that robbed me of my innocence, but they are buried deep in my psyche, probably for my own good.

When my mother and father came to pick us up, I remember running to my mother and burying my face in her skirt and sobbing. When asked why I was crying, however, I was unable to tell her what her father had done to me. Years later, I told a friend about this experience, and she insisted I confront my mother, the person who should have protected me. "You won't be able to heal yourself until you do," she'd warned. I could tell my mother just about anything, but not this. Until this very moment, I never understood why, I just knew she would not be able to hear what I had to say.

Before I had a chance to censor myself, I blurted out, "Granddaddy wasn't very nice to you, was he, Mom?"

She was quick to reassure me, "Oh yes, he was nice. He was very nice. He was just fine!"

I took her hand, looked into her eyes, and said, "Mom, I know he wasn't nice to you, but it wasn't your fault, you were just a little girl."

In that moment, with those words that flowed through me, I knew we were both being healed. My mother took a couple of deep breaths, as if to clear the unpleasant memories from her lungs, her body, and her heart.

I said, "I think it will be Billy who will meet you. What do you think?"

My Uncle Bill was my mother's youngest brother, born when she was nine years old. She had taken care of him when he was a baby and years later went to visit him every month when he was a tuberculosis patient in an iron lung at a sanitarium just south of San Francisco. She would leave Court and me under a weeping willow tree with a lunch basket and a blanket to sit on during those visits, and we would watch the gardener glide his big mower over the sanitarium's expansive lawn. Bill spent the last 10 years of his life in that iron lung and died when he was just 28 years old.

"Yes, Billy. Billy will meet me," my mother said as she squeezed my hand, sighed, and slipped back into sleep, this time with a smile on her face. She would be with family when she got to where she was going, a comforting thought for me as well.

Eleanor Grace Zimmerman Mumford, born March 5, 1911, died June 27, 1993. Though my mother didn't really understand my dedication to my work, she was a kind woman who supported not only me, but others who needed help, no matter who they were. Whatever resentments I may have had from growing up with an abusive father and a mother who was not equipped to defend me were resolved long before her death. I felt only gratitude that I was able to ease her journey from this world into the next.

●●●

The second week of July 2007, I received a phone call from my sister-in-law, Janis, who told me my brother, Courtland Mumford, had been missing since July 7. I talked with Court several times a year, and he had lived with us for a while when he and his wife were separated, but I had not heard from him recently. He had taken off in his Piper Cub light aircraft from Aurora Airport, just south of Portland, Oregon, a week earlier and had never returned.

Court was 21 months younger than me. As adults, we had always had a congenial relationship. I remember one morning when Court and I were running along the water on the cool wet sand of Stinson Beach, north of the Golden Gate Bridge. Court knew about the work I was doing and wanted to talk to me about it. He said, "I've given this a lot of thought, Marilyn, and I'm glad I was circumcised."

A few months later, I showed Court *Informed Consent,* the video Sheila and I made that revealed just five minutes of what the baby was enduring and how he reacted to being circumcised. Court was deeply disturbed by the screams of the baby. It took time before he was able to acknowledge his own loss and to admit he would have preferred to have had a choice. But he did. As a convert to the cause, he went on to save several babies and proudly told me about each one.

Like me, Court had left home early because of our abusive father, joining the Navy and spending four years on a nuclear missile submarine. While he was in the Navy, I was demonstrating on the streets of San Francisco against the Vietnam War. After the Navy, Court got a pilot's license and flew for TWA until his 60th birthday, when it was time to retire.

Court was a tri-athlete—a swimmer, bicyclist, and marathon runner. When he was training for the Iron Man Triathlon in 1982, I created healthy cookie and brownie recipes he could make that would give him energy, strength, and stamina, both during his training and the triathlon. In return, Court gave me a plane ticket to Hawaii so that I could join him on the Big Island for his first triathlon. After his 2.5-mile swim and 114-mile bike ride, I ran some of the last marathon miles with him. Court ran his 100th marathon on his 50th birthday. Over the next few years, he participated in six or seven triathlons and had been training again for another.

Court's love of flying continued after his retirement. When he learned that the Piper Cub, an American light aircraft (puddle jumper) manufactured between 1937 and 1947, was being reissued, he ordered one. He told the manufacturer not to install a transponder, however, a device required by law that reveals the plane's location, because he wanted to order his own. He was only allowed to fly within a 30-mile radius without a transponder but had been practicing take offs and landings. The Air National Guard searched for him, using a grid over the entire 30-mile radius for more than two weeks, but never found the Tonka-truck-yellow airplane.

The day before they called off the search, I remember working in my garden and bursting into tears with the realization that I would never again see my beloved brother's handsome face, his broad smile, or his beautiful blue eyes. Not knowing where Court was left lots of room for speculation. My greatest fear during the time they searched was that he was alive, injured, and in pain. Would they find him in time for needed medical help? My son Troy said, "Mom, just think of Court with the throttle in one hand and a bottle of tequila in the other on his way to Mexico."

I have lost many people who walked this path with me over the years. I miss their companionship, courage, and energy in fighting the medical establishment and the status quo. And I have mourned all the babies who have been subjected to unnecessary circumcision. Their wounds are seared into my soul. I expected the loss of my mother, but I will never know what happened to my brother. I think of him every day.

Chapter 17

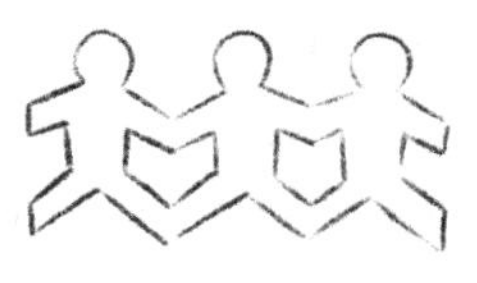

LEARNING FROM MY MISTAKES

With a few years of experience under my belt, I had to admit that, although we had effectively debunked the medical mythology behind circumcision, we were not getting through to those who performed circumcisions—obstetricians and pediatricians—and those who informed parents about circumcision—nurses. The evidence we had gathered and presented against routine infant circumcision was irrefutable, but the medical establishment either didn't want to hear us or didn't want to change.

After two symposia in California, it made sense to shift our efforts to the opposite side of the country. I chose the University of Maryland as the site of the 3rd International Symposium on Circumcision, May 22-25, 1994, to bring the message to a different audience—students and academics—plus it was only a few miles from the nation's capitol. East Coast friends of NOCIRC guaranteed they would "pack the house," which sounded good to me.

I also decided that it was time to take a different tack with this symposium. By this time, I understood that circumcision was not a medical issue, but rather a human rights concern. It was thus our moral, ethical, and legal responsibility to defend the right of both males and females to genital autonomy, and we needed to involve lawyers and the legal system as stakeholders in the crusade.

As I was searching for a keynote speaker with name recognition, Jim Bigelow, a California colleague who wrote *The Joy of Uncircumcising!*, remembered hearing comedian and Civil Rights activist Dick Gregory talk about the trauma of being tricked into a circumcision at age 15. Gregory, who began performing in segregated nightclubs in 1961, had become the first Black comedian to cross over to white audiences via TV and record albums. At first, he used comedy to support his stance on racial equality and the Civil Rights Movement, but then interrupted his successful entertainment career to devote his energy to full-time activism. Participating in nonviolent protests, he was beaten and jailed many times, but never gave up his commitment to his cause.

When Ken and I picked up Gregory from the airport and drove him to the university hotel, we had time to talk. I knew he would be aware of Lenny Bruce's precedent of political and cultural satire and told him I worked for Lenny from 1963 to 1966. He quickly pulled out his cell phone to call his wife and tell her. They both appreciated Lenny's work.

Gregory's keynote address on Sunday night described the excruciating pain he had suffered from his circumcision. Perhaps even more traumatic was his loss of trust in his mother, who had tricked him into going to the doctor's office with no hint of what was to happen. There was no medical reason for the surgery. His perspective was that "circumcision of males and females creates violence, creates hostile activity."

The next day, we heard presentations on the "paradigms and politics of circumcision," the horror of "unnecessary sexual surgery," and the normalcy of foreskins in Australia. We also screened two documentary films, *Nurses of St. Vincent: Saying No to Circumcision* by Barry Ellsworth, and *Fire Eyes,* Somali filmmaker and activist Soraya Miré's breathtaking work about female genital mutilation.

Tuesday talks included religious considerations of circumcision from the perspectives of Evangelical Christianity, Islam, and the Jewish tradition. We were thrilled to have as a speaker Sami Aldeeb Abu-Sahlieh, an attorney with the Swiss Institute of Comparative Law in Lausanne, Switzerland, a Palestinian Christian, and a religious scholar. Not only did Aldeeb understand law and human rights, but he had much to offer in terms of the ritualistic meaning of religious rites with their moral and ethical connotations. He made the point that neither judicial logic nor morality can make a legitimate distinction between female and male circumcision. In other words, we can't say one (female genital mutilation) is damaging to the physical integrity of a child without acknowledging the harm of the other (male genital mutilation).

Breakout sessions on female genital cutting followed Sami Aldeeb's presentation. Soraya Miré shared the story of her own genital cutting at the age of 13. Her mother had promised to take her for a special gift, which Soraya assumed would be a new dress. Instead, her mother allowed Soraya to be held down and anesthetized in preparation for the clitoridectomy and infibulation she would suffer and endure. Soraya quietly and bravely told us, "I will never forget the sound of the cutting of the flesh between my legs." We all wept for this beautiful woman who was willing to tell her tragic story to expose the practice and to help others. Soraya has dedicated her life to bringing an end to the genital mutilation of *all* children. Her book *The Girl with Three Legs*, was published in 2011. A screenplay based on Soraya's book has been written. She now is working toward its production.

At our bookstore and exhibit area, Australian Elizabeth Nobel proudly displayed copies of *The Joy of Being a Boy!*, a booklet she and her husband, obstetrician Leo Sorger, had just published. Elizabeth struggled during the process of publication because the printer called authorities about the book's photos of her nude young son, which were meant to help parents feel comfortable about the intact penis and to help boys to know that their intact bodies are normal.

A few years later when I displayed the book at our booth at an American Academy of Pediatrics National Convention, an American pediatrician came up to me and said, "My wife is disturbed by the obscene photo on the cover of this book."

I asked him, "What about the normal body does she find obscene?"

He stomped off without another word. I suspect he was as offended as his wife but didn't have the courage to admit it, so he blamed her. I wondered how, with an attitude like that, he was able to examine children in a way that respects them and helps them feel relaxed and comfortable about their bodies.

At the closing banquet of our symposium, Thomas Szasz, MD, psychoanalyst and author of *The Myth of Mental Illness* and *The Manufacture of Madness*, gave a fascinating and challenging presentation. In his talk, titled "Routine Neonatal Circumcision: Symbol of the Birth of the Therapeutic State," Szasz stated, "I believe the time has come to acknowledge that the practice of routine circumcision rests on the absurd premise that the only mammal in creation born in the condition that requires immediate surgical correction is the human male." Amen!

● ● ●

Although the content of the symposium was amazing, and the presenters and attendees were extraordinarily committed, I was terribly disappointed that only 100 people were in attendance in a university auditorium with 500 seats.

How did this happen?

Until my arrival at the symposium, I was unaware that the person who had enthusiastically promised to do all the media work hadn't done what he'd promised. There had been no promotion of the event whatsoever—not even in the University's own newspaper. The only thing I was able to do was to show up at the campus radio station and hope to make a plug. The radio host invited me to come in and talk on air after I conveyed to him what was happening on campus. We picked up a few student attendees through my efforts.

It was difficult seeing all those empty seats, especially with someone like Dick Gregory giving our keynote address. But Gregory said something pertinent and reassuring to us. "Don't feel bad if the seats at your events are not all filled. When we started the Civil Rights Movement, we couldn't pay people to take a seat at our events. Just keep doing what you're doing because it is vitally important!"

I learned my lesson and never again left the promotion of such an important event to someone I did not know personally.

Chapter 18

SUPPORT FOR CIRCUMCISION AS A HUMANITARIAN ISSUE GROWS

About 10 years after being forced to resign from my nursing position at Marin General Hospital (MGH), with the help of a nursing student at the College of Marin, I organized a conference for nurses and other concerned individuals. The day after the conference, we planned a mile walk from the college to Marin General Hospital to demonstrate there. Then I received a call from the nursing student telling me the nursing school would not allow the conference to be held at the college because of our planned demonstration. The School of Nursing, she explained, needed to be in the good graces of the hospital so that their students would be allowed to do clinical practice there.

The issue of circumcision was still as much of a bureaucratic political game as when I had worked at MGH. This reminded me of Lenny Bruce's inability to book engagements at nightclubs that had successfully hosted him prior to his being found guilty of obscenity charges in New York. Afterwards, any venue that tried to feature Lenny would face retribution in the form of being shut down by authorities based on some flimsy excuse. And so it was with MGH and the threat of affecting the viability of the nursing program if a peaceful demonstration against routine infant circumcision was involved. I found another venue.

Our July 28th, 1994, conference was well-attended. The following day people gathered in the parking lot across the street from the College of Marin in preparation for our walk to the hospital.

As I got out of my car and said to no one in particular, "Oh no, I forgot my camera," I heard a soft voice behind me say, "I've got a camera!" I turned to see James Loewen's smiling face. This talented Canadian photographer planned on documenting this event just as he had our earlier demonstrations. We could not have asked for a better person to document in photographs the history we were making.

Photo by James Loewen

Once we arrived at Marin General Hospital, we walked up and down the street with our signs protesting genital cutting of infants. An administrator came out to speak with us. He said, "This is a quiet zone; it is a hospital."

I understood, of course, that patients heal faster in a peaceful environment. By the mid-1990s, however, patients were more disturbed by noise inside hospitals than outside: equipment beeping, ringing, and buzzing, carts clattering along hallways, staff laughing and joking, the constant waking up and checking for vital signs. The volume of our demonstration was nothing compared to the decibel level of normal hospital activity 24 hours a day.

Later the same year, Frank Cranbourne, Director of NOCIRC of Seattle, organized a conference and a demonstration at Olympic Medical Supply. The conscientious objector nurses came from Santa Fe, New Mexico, and a group of us who lived nearby or who had driven to Seattle for the occasion met them at the airport with balloons and signs welcoming and honoring them. The next day, we gathered at a park and walked to Olympic Medical, where Circumstraints, the plastic molded boards with four-point restraints that hold babies' arms and legs down for circumcision, are manufactured.

Halley Baker and Matthew Orlando (Photo by James Loewen)

Matthew G., George Denniston, MD (Photos by James Loewen)

Demonstrators placed flowers on a Circumstraint in front of the office doors as Tim Hammond played a recording of the screams of a newborn baby boy being circumcised for employees inside to hear.

At the end of our demonstration, Mary Conant and I went inside and offered flowers to the company's spokesperson, but he refused to take them. He said we were trespassing and told us to leave. In keeping with the theme of our message, the demonstration ended peacefully, just as it had begun.

●●●

Protests coupled with education efforts were having an effect domestically. In Wisconsin, Assembly Bill 365 "prohibiting circumcision, excision or infibulation of certain genital tissue of a female minor and providing a penalty" became effective May 28, 1995.[45] Anyone found to be in violation of that law could be fined a maximum of $10,000, imprisoned for a maximum of five years, or both. At least females were beginning to be protected from genital cutting.

With the help of Harry Meislahn, Director of NOCIRC of Illinois, NOCIRC and other circumcision education organizations held a

Strategy Summit in Chicago to coincide with the April 1995 American Academy of Pediatrics National Convention. Many doctors still claimed no one had ever complained about their circumcision, but now pediatricians could see men protesting what had been done to them without their consent. As a result of projects like *Whose Body, Whose Rights?*, a video documentary by Lawrence Dillon and Tim Hammond narrated by my son Troy that premiered on KQED TV in the San Francisco Bay Area, many doctors could no longer claim ignorance.[46]

The Colorado State Judiciary Committee voted to pass a bill that branded female genital mutilation (FGM) as blatant child abuse.[47] Introduced by Senator Dorothy Rupert, who was inspired by a 16-year-old Kenyan who became a victim of FGM at the age of seven that Rupert met at a UN Women's Conference, the bill states that culture or custom are no defense for mutilation. Rupert was able to make FGM a felony in Colorado, with criminal penalties against practitioners and parents who force their daughter to undergo the procedure, including transporting a female under the age of 16 to another state for the purpose of FGM.[48]

Even though no bills protecting the bodily integrity and genital autonomy rights of male minors have been passed, our Constitution, state laws against battery and false imprisonment (strapping babies down), and several international documents, including the *UN Declaration on Human Rights* and the *UN Convention on the Rights of the Child,* make it clear that every person has a right to safety of their person. Cutting off normal parts of babies without their consent is against our laws, laws that continue to be ignored and violated every day.

Although I was encouraged by this progress, U.S. doctors were still not "getting" the fact that unnecessary circumcision was male genital mutilation. The next step for NOCIRC was to hold a symposium in Europe. My hope was that international attention and interest among medical professionals would make American physicians either listen to reason or be ashamed of themselves in front of their international colleagues for continuing to perform non-therapeutic circumcision on non-consenting minors.

Chapter 19

AN INTERNATIONAL SYMPOSIUM

Sami Aldeeb Abu-Sahlieh of the Swiss Institute of Comparative Law in Lausanne, who had spoken at our University of Maryland symposium, offered to co-sponsor our 1996 symposium at the University of Lausanne. Administrators there didn't want us to use the word *circumcision* in our symposium title for fear it would offend Jews and Muslims, so we changed the name of this symposium to International Symposium on Sexual Mutilations. Although it may sound harsher, it more accurately reflects what is done to infants and children and surprisingly was more palatable to our hosts.

On August 3, Sheila, Tina Kimmel (one of our many Jewish intactivists), Ken, and I flew from San Francisco to Paris, where we were met by Dr. Michel Odent (to whom I will always be grateful for agreeing to be my one international expert at our first symposium). Michel had made reservations for us at a hotel across the street from the Paris-Sorbonne University where he had gone to medical school. We checked in, then went to dinner at an outdoor café to celebrate both Sheila's birthday and our first trip to Europe. We stayed up as long as we could after our long flight and the nine-hour time difference, but by 7pm we were ready for bed.

At 11pm, Ken and I were awakened by the sounds of Parisian nightlife and ventured outside to join in. We walked to a nearby square that was filled with people and took a table at a restaurant where couples and families sat with coffee or wine, enjoying the warm August evening.

Ken and I watched a mother and father sip their coffee, smoke cigarettes, and chat as their two young children played nearby. The children were walking up and down a little curb when suddenly the blond, curly haired girl of about four slipped and landed on her knee, scraping it. She began to cry and limped toward her mother. Her dark-haired brother, who looked to be about six, followed. The mother looked at the girl's knee, then lit into her son, evidently chastising him for allowing it to happen. He seemed to be trying to explain it wasn't his fault, but his mother kept on until she ran out of steam. Since the conversation was in French, we had no idea what they were saying, but being parents, we could guess.

When the boy saw us observing this little drama, he walked toward us and stood on the sidewalk in front of us, telling us his side of the story. We nodded our heads as though we understood French. He became more animated, taking off his dark-rimmed glasses and holding them in his hand, his arms gesturing this way and that as he explained what had happened. We nodded more to reassure him. Finally, he put his glasses back on, smiled at us in relief, and returned to the table to join his sister and parents.

Ken and I were deeply touched by our exchange with this boy on our first night in Paris. I had never communicated so intimately with another person whose language I didn't speak. We didn't understand the words the boy was speaking, but we could feel what he was saying and convey that we were sympathetic and cared. As the movement to end circumcision grew, we learned this simple lesson over and over again: energetic connection needs no language and knows no international boundaries.

From Paris, we took the high-speed train to Switzerland, where we were met by Sami Aldeeb. He took us to his home in St. Sulpice, a suburb of Lausanne on the shore of Lac Léman (Lake Geneva), where we met his wife and two lovely daughters. We stayed at their home, which was close to the university, and walked there every morning during the symposium.

The next day we visited a Romanesque church, built in 1100 CE as a part of a monastery. No one was in the church when we arrived, so I stood behind the pulpit and decreed a New Covenant, "I say to you, every child from this day forward shall be protected from genital cutting." When I came down from my high place, Sami told Ken and me that people came from all over the world to get married there. He suggested that Ken and I get married while we were there, and we thought it a beautiful idea. For the next two days, we could hardly speak to one another and kept laughing at our reactions to the idea of marriage. Ken had never been married and I had been married twice. Although it was a lovely, romantic dream in a place such as this, I was not eager to embark on that journey again. For the past 30 years plus, we have felt it best not to ruin a good relationship by getting the government involved in our personal business.

The University of Lausanne on the shores of Lake Léman in the town of Dorigny provided a beautiful setting for our 1996 symposium. One of the oldest continuously operating universities in Europe (founded in 1537), the site had gravitas not found in the United States and was a perfect setting for the seriousness of the issue we were about to address now from ethical and legal perspectives. As a first-time traveler to Europe, I was enthralled with the modernized campus with its magnificent views of the lake and the French and Swiss Alps.

James DeMeo, presenting "The Geography of Male and Female Genital Mutilation," began by explaining, "The desire by adults to attack the genitals of their infants and young children with sharp knives is a subject about which a tremendous amount has been written, the majority of which attempts to justify and 'explain' it, but in a manner which leaves the larger cultural-social backdrop uncriticized." He went on to say he would take a different approach, not only criticizing that "backdrop," but "lifting it up and getting a good look at what's going on 'behind the curtain' of this deeply emotional and brutal human drama."[49]

DeMeo originally had studied genital mutilations "as a part of a larger investigation of the geographical and cross-cultural aspects of human behavior among subsistence-level, aboriginal peoples." He concluded his presentation by describing genital mutilations of young males and females as "major examples of cultural 'traits' or 'practices' which, on deeper analysis, reveal roots in severe pleasure-anxiety, with sadistic overtones...related to anti-sexual, anti-female, hierarchical, obedience-demanding, patriarchal authoritarian characteristics."[50]

This was a different cultural perspective for me as it was based on the study of aboriginal peoples, but I couldn't help thinking: *and there you have it, ladies and gentlemen. Are our western "civilized" societies so different?*

France's renowned sexologist Dr. Gerard Zwang spoke about how sexual pathways are "potential" pathways, like the path that forms across a field of grass when people begin walking across it. "Orgasm," he said, "is a complex systemic reflex. It encompasses numerous pathways and nervous connections of such magnitude that one can speak of a vast orgasmic circuit." He explained that it is by use that sexual pathways are formed and, when sexual organs are altered shortly after birth, normal pathways are unable to form.

This rang true to me, after having been exposed to so many personal narratives of the long-term impact of circumcision. I believe that—along with neglecting the possibility and then the evidence that babies feel pain—the medical establishment and scientists are still in denial that the circuitry for our sexual development might be present at birth.

Robert Van Howe asked, "Why Does Neonatal Circumcision Persist in the United States?" and proceeded to answer the question. A pediatrician and public health expert, Bob mentioned the landmark study by Douglas Gairdner, published in 1949 in *The British Medical Journal*, that disproved the alleged justifications for circumcision; it was this, he said, along with the British National Health Service's decision to no longer pay for routine circumcision, that resulted in a remarkable drop in the circumcision rate in England.[51] Meanwhile, he continued, "The American medical establishment has remained a fee-for-service system," not only allowing but actually encouraging the practice.

That comparison with perhaps the most culturally similar country to the United States (we adopted many of our medical theories and practices from England) seemed to me to speak volumes. When the incentive for profit was removed from British doctors, circumcision became a non-essential surgery for healthy infants.

I was being exposed to more perspectives and learning more. I knew the other attendees from the U.S. felt the same.

The last presentation, "The Ashley Montagu Resolution to End the Genital Mutilation of Children Worldwide: A Petition to the World Court, The Hague," was presented by James W. Prescott, PhD. Even though it was supported by Francis H.C. Crick, PhD, Jonas Salk, MD, Ashley Montagu, PhD, Thomas Szasz, MD, and others of note, more than 25 years later it still needs to be submitted to the World Court by a head of state, which I challenge my readers to remedy. It is long past due, and I would like to know that this has been done in my time.[52]

I was gratified that this conference was attended by representatives from Amnesty International, the World Health Organization, and the United Nations. After one presentation on the problem of male sexual mutilation in the United States, a member of the United Nations said to NOCIRC representatives, "This is very disturbing information. Thank you for presenting the truth. I had no idea this was going on in a civilized country."

Knowing the truth is the first step to taking action.

The proceedings of this symposium were the first to be published in book form by Springer Publishing, in *Sexual Mutilations: A Human Tragedy,* edited by George C. Denniston and Marilyn Fayre Milos (1997). Someone at Springer had seen an ad for our symposium in *Nature* magazine and contacted NOCIRC. Thus began a relationship between the symposia and Springer, which went on to print seven more books containing papers from presenters. The royalties have never been significant, but they went into the NOCIRC bank account.

Chapter 20

THE EMOTIONAL TOLL OF THIS WORK

We held our next symposium in England, which may have gotten it wrong to begin with—setting the stage for false beliefs about the benefits of circumcision curing a dozen or so diseases. But the British healthcare system had come to its senses by dropping medically unnecessary circumcision coverage.

At the conclusion of this symposium, held at the venerable Oxford University in August 1998, my heart was full because we had brought together international experts and amassed a wealth of information on bodily integrity, genital autonomy, and how the genital cutting of infants and children violates existing national and international laws. People were talking about the issues now. It was so important that we were holding our symposia in various countries worldwide to advance the idea of protecting children from the pain, trauma, and consequences of genital cutting. Our books of the proceedings of our symposia, published by Springer, would provide concerned experts another avenue for distributing their work into university libraries worldwide.

As usual, there was no down time to process and savor my reflections. Although I had read all the abstracts prior to the Oxford symposium, listened to all the talks, and read and re-read the papers after the symposium in preparation for editing our book on the proceedings, during my final reading of Dr. Robert Van Howe's paper on types of pain medication and their efficacy during circumcision I suffered an emotional collapse.

Because I feel such empathy and compassion for the babies, I have had to learn to do the work to stop circumcision without being continuously distraught. Unlike the emotional detachment medical students and doctors in the U.S. develop, my challenge was to take care every single day to focus on the positive developments that have happened since I began this work. I know from experience that maintaining my resilience in the face of disappointment is vital. But every so often something comes at me when my guard is down, and I am not prepared to protect myself.

Reading through Van Howe's paper from the symposium, I suddenly realized that, not only did pain medication *not* eliminate or alleviate the pain of genital cutting, but in each of the studies done to determine efficacy of a product or method of pain relief there was a *control group* of babies that received *no* pain relief at all! These studies were carried out years after Anand and Hickey had demonstrated the pain responses of infants and showed that the younger the infant, the more devastatingly the pain is perceived and experienced.[53] Thus, continuing attempts to determine pain responses in babies and to use babies as controls for pain studies was, and always will be, unconscionable.

I spent the next six weeks crying. *How could humans have become so desensitized and inhumane?* Animals demonstrate more empathy than humans, and we often seem to have more empathy for our animals than we do for our children. I didn't stop working during that tearful period. In fact, it heightened my determination and renewed my sense of purpose. But it was exhausting to feel the sadness of so much needless pain and suffering inflicted on babies and children, both male and female. Aren't life's challenges hard enough to navigate without taking a baby from his mother's arms to face gratuitous surgery alone?

I have experienced many such moments of devastation. Still, reading fluctuating circumcision statistics year after year or the American Academy of Pediatrics' wishy-washy, self-serving statements have never been enough for me to totally burn out. How can I when babies continue to be delivered up as sacrificial lambs to the medical establishment, which persists in misleading and confusing parents who honestly want to do the right thing?

In the early days, I thought I might be able to stop this human tragedy through making vital information about circumcision available to everyone. I didn't yet understand how long it takes for social change to occur in the face of personal denial, cultural conditioning, religious indoctrination, medical deception, and financial incentive. People do not readily admit they've held the wrong position, profited from it, or harmed someone because of it.

Over the years, many people I've met in the intactivist movement have had to pull back from this work for one reason or another. It can be mind-bending, mind-boggling, and mind-blowing. I understand that people who do what I do need to take a break at times. But there is so much more to do. As Jim Snyder once said to me, "Marilyn, you're going to die in the saddle."

Chapter 21

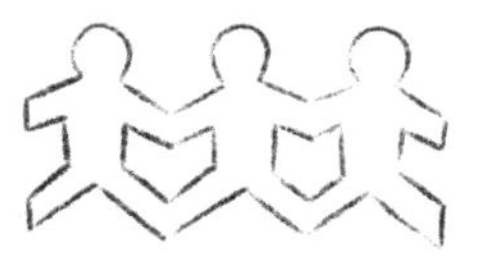

CLASHING WITH THE AMERICAN ACADEMY OF PEDIATRICS

As you may have guessed by now, the American Academy of Pediatrics (AAP) has never been a friend to those who want to spare infants the pain and trauma of circumcision.

In 1997, the AAP selected another Task Force Committee on Circumcision for the preparation of a new position paper. NOCIRC was asked to submit materials that would be of interest. No problem! This was the inside track we were hoping for to spread accurate information about circumcision to pediatricians, information that in turn would be disseminated to the public. We sent more than 90 articles and studies that had been published since the Task Force's last position paper. Perhaps the tide would be turned.

Yet, after years of being one of the exhibitors at the annual AAP convention, NOCIRC was not permitted to host a booth in 1998. AAP leaders were worried that a NOCIRC presence might create a stir. This came as a surprise and made me uneasy and angry. We had always maintained a civilized presence at the convention. And our clearinghouse for information on circumcision was considered reliable enough for the AAP Task Force to request article referrals from us. I didn't realize it then, but this was a sure sign that our influence was getting stronger.

My presence was felt anyway, as I stood outside the Moscone Convention Center with other demonstrators. We asked pediatricians coming and going to the convention what it would take to change their mind about circumcision. Among the notable responses:

I'd be delighted if I never had to do another one. The question is to have the moral courage not to do it. - Anonymous

It's the obstetricians who do the circumcisions and for them it's economics. We pediatricians don't challenge them because we need their referrals. - Anonymous

If I changed my mind, I'd have to put a gun to my head. - Retired pediatrician who claims to have circumcised 10,000 babies during his career.

A million dollars. - Thomas Wiswell, MD

On January 15, 1999, by the way, Thomas Wiswell—the doctor who promoted circumcision to prevent urinary tract infections (UTIs) in baby boys even though antibiotics would cure the malady—amputated a baby's foreskin on the ABC 20/20 news program on national television. I saw with my own eyes that even though Wiswell injected the baby twice with an anesthetic, the baby's pitiful cries didn't stop during the surgery. Other anesthetized, crying babies were shown, too. The public was becoming more aware and informed as parents could see circumcision causes pain and suffering, even when analgesic is used.

In an about-face, NOCIRC once again was invited to have a booth at the AAP's National Convention in 1999. The Task Force on Circumcision had completed its report and was showcasing its new position statement.[54] Perhaps AAP leadership felt that NOCIRC would appreciate a slightly softened stance by the Task Force and quit bugging them. But how could we until the AAP acknowledged that circumcision was completely unnecessary and of no benefit to a child's health?

Once again, the AAP had disregarded the wellbeing of the babies it serves by remaining on the fence about the necessity of circumcision and deferring the decision solely to parents. Since parents relied on pediatricians, obstetricians, and nursing staff to educate them about the benefits and risks of circumcision—while the medical establishment denied responsibility for doing so—parents' chances of being informed consumers were low.

We were relieved to see that the AAP—while not truly standing for the rights of the child—at least recognized that **the benefits of circumcision really do *not* outweigh the risks of circumcision**, as evidenced by the following points:

The risk of urinary tract infections (UTI) is low in male infants.

Penile cancer is a rare disease and occurs in both circumcised and intact men.

Behavioral factors are far more important than circumcision status in the risk of acquiring HIV.

Circumcision without analgesia is painful and stressful for newborns (although the AAP failed to mention that no analgesia is both safe to use and eliminates the pain of circumcision).

Finally, while the report stated that the complication rate of circumcision is unknown, it acknowledged this:

[D]ocumented complications include bleeding, infection, recurrent phimosis, wound separation, concealed penis, skin bridges, meatal stenosis, inclusion cysts, retained Plastibell device, sepsis, partial amputation of the glans, and penile necrosis, as well as others mentioned or not.

Left out was the scientific literature documenting the rich erogenous innervation and the many functions of the foreskin, even while acknowledging "reports that penile sensation and sexual satisfaction are decreased for circumcised males." Further, no mention was made of the legal experts and medical ethicists in the U.S., Canada, and Europe who question the legality of non-therapeutic circumcision and have determined that it constitutes a violation of human rights.

So, while this Task Force had undone some of the damage done ten years earlier by Edgar Schoen's Task Force, there would be no gold star from us.

When several AAP officials came to the NOCIRC booth to speak with me at the 1999 convention, I showed them the errors in their most current pamphlet. For example, it said, "One day the foreskin will separate from the glans. This is called foreskin retraction." No. Separation of foreskin and the glans is what makes foreskin retraction *possible.* I went over their pamphlet line by line, correcting it for them. "I'm not trying to be argumentative," I said. "I am trying to make your handout on this issue accurate." I did this several times over the years as each new pamphlet came out. With each revision, they got a little closer to accuracy.

Because our circumcising doctors and our circumcising society are unfamiliar with foreskins, this lack of accuracy was understandable. The majority of male American doctors don't even have foreskins. Still, shouldn't physicians who were altering people's lives have picked up on these errors in basic anatomy?

The reason for their ignorance doesn't matter, I had to remind myself. The evidence is available in journals, videos, and on websites and was potentially right in front of them if the articles NOCIRC submitted were distributed. *Why was I making excuses for them?* Their lack of accuracy was not acceptable.

When I began my work in 1979, circumcision was nearly ubiquitous, with Edward Wallerstein estimating that 85 percent of baby boys born in the United States were subjected to genital cutting within hours after birth.[55] Twenty years later, I was hearing anecdotally from more and more mothers that they were keeping their baby boys intact, but because there is no mandatory reporting of circumcision surgeries, it has always been difficult to determine the rate with any certainty.

Ten years later, at the 2009 AAP National Convention in Washington, D.C., we realized the one thing that was consistent was that most of the doctors who stopped by our booth were not from the United States. European doctors often told us how shocked they were to learn that U.S. doctors were routinely circumcising newborn boys without medical indication. When we asked them to help educate American doctors, their response went something like this: "American doctors will never give up doing circumcisions because they are greedy, and circumcision is an easy way to make money." Sadly, American doctors have not yet proved European doctors wrong.

While they did not embrace circumcision, doctors from Latin America told us they had been taught to retract a baby's foreskin and wash under it. They were surprised to learn that premature retraction of the foreskin is contraindicated for infants and children and, in fact, is harmful. Non-retractability is a protective attribute of the infant foreskin during the first few years of life. It needs only to be washed on the outside, like the finger of a child is washed—from body to tip. These doctors were willing and eager to learn from us and often would return to our booth the next year to thank us.

Meanwhile, most U.S. pediatricians attending the convention stayed away from our booth.

In September 2012—in what can only be described as a last-ditch effort to defend and perpetuate an indefensible cultural practice—the AAP Task Force on Circumcision came out with another *Circumcision Policy Statement* to update the Academy's 1999 recommendations. This new Task Force, after five years of meetings, deliberations, and cherry-picking research, essentially produced another sales pitch for neonatal circumcision,[56] judging that the benefits of newborn male circumcision—i.e., prevention of urinary tract infections, penile cancer, and transmission of some sexually transmitted infections, including HIV—outweighed the risks. The American College of Obstetricians and Gynecologists endorsed the statement.

Does it make sense to say I was flabbergasted and yet not surprised? If any one of the physicians on the Task Force had ever attended a NOCIRC symposium they would know, without a doubt, that endorsing circumcision for these benefits was misleading, wrong, and a disservice to all parents and health workers, including physicians, in the United States.

Although the report admitted that there is *not enough evidence* to recommend routine infant circumcision for *all* baby boys, it provided no guidance at all about how parents (deemed, again, the parties responsible for making the decision) might assess whether their own sons might benefit from this procedure. This was an alarming statement because historically *no records have been kept on risks,* including botched circumcisions, complications, long-term harm, or deaths. In fact, the report stated there are no accurate statistics on risks and, when questioned, one of the Task Force members said they just "felt" the benefits outweighed the risks. *So much for scientific credibility.*

Interestingly, the AAP Task Force Report also suggested that older boys and young men should be informed about the "benefits" of circumcision. *On what basis?* This would have broken my heart if it didn't make me so mad. Now the AAP was targeting intact boys who may have been spared in the past decades because of our work (which, by the way, has always emphasized that we oppose child circumcision *unless it is medically necessary*, which is rare).

In addition, the report added that it is reasonable for doctors to be paid for doing circumcisions. Why even bring that up in a report such as this? Was it an issue that they were charged with exploring? Or was this an attempt to get Medicaid and insurance companies who had defunded circumcision over the past few years to begin paying for it again? Or an attempt to lure parents into believing the surgery was necessary and therefore they should invest their own dollars in ensuring it was done or lobby their insurance companies to cover circumcision if they did not? Infant circumcision in the United Kingdom virtually disappeared once the British Health System stopped covering it. Mainstream pediatricians and obstetricians in the United States apparently did not want to see that money train come to an end.

This AAP Report was released the same year the European Academy of Paediatrics came out with its own statement, which was unbiased and clear.

> *There is no compelling evidence that neonatal circumcision is indicated for preventive or hygienic reasons. Given the lack of benefits and the risk for short- and long-term complications, there are insufficient arguments to justify non-therapeutic neonatal circumcision. If circumcision might prove to prevent sexually transmitted diseases, then the procedure can be done at an age the boy himself can make a well-informed decision.*[57]

What a relief to read something reasonable and evidence-based from a professional pediatric organization. In fact, **there is no national medical organization in the world that recommends routine circumcision of male infants.**[58]

Here is the difference between the AAP and other countries. *The AAP was focused not on the safety of babies, but on shifting the responsibility of (and liability for) circumcision to parents and on ensuring that doctors continue to be paid for circumcision.*

Chapter 22

PROTESTORS JONATHON CONTE AND THE BLOODSTAINED MEN

In October 2012 I was in the security line at the San Francisco airport as I headed to catch my plane to New Orleans for a protest outside the American Academy of Pediatrics (AAP) National Convention when I heard someone call my name. It was Jonathon Conte, a young man who had moved to San Francisco a few years earlier to join the Intactivist Movement and was going to the AAP protest as well. He was one of the leaders of the Bay Area Intactivists and had worked diligently to get signatures for the circumcision ban in San Francisco. An extremely sensitive man with a beautiful smile and a heart to match, Jonathon spoke intelligently and calmly about the harm of circumcision and influenced many in his kind and gentle way. I was happy we were able to sit together on the plane. Jonathon posted our picture on his Facebook page while we were in the air.

Photo by Jonathon Conte

He told me about a photo he had seen of Richard Duncker—founder of the London-based website *Men Do Complain* and Master of Ceremonies at several of our symposia—in an outfit he'd made for a demonstration in London in 2010. It was white painter coveralls with a splotch of red on the crotch to symbolize blood from a circumcision. Jonathon had made one for himself plus six more for the protest. "Do you think other men will put them on and join me?" he asked. I had no doubt and assured him that they would.

The next morning, we set up our spot across the street from the front doors of the New Orleans Convention Center. At the corner was a parking lot for the hotel next to it. It had a chain-link fence around it. Outside the fence was a bus stop with two benches, which we were happy to have available to us. The hotel had a coffee shop, food, and bathrooms we could use as needed. The parking lot manager allowed us to park our rental van, with signs and handouts, and also gave us permission to hang a large banner produced by Intact America on the fence. The banner's large heading, "I DID NOT CONSENT," could be seen from the steps and from inside the large windows on the first and second floors of the Convention Center. It featured photos of 22 different men, each holding a photo of himself when he was a baby. Every one of the thousands of pediatricians and sponsors who entered or left the building had to pass it.

Photo from intactamerica.org

It didn't take long for AAP conference organizers to bring a policeman across the street to the corner where we were gathered. The police officer told the AAP officials we were well within our rights to be there. After all, this was a peaceful demonstration, we had permission to hang the banner, and we were on a public sidewalk. The AAP representatives were not pleased but there was nothing they could do about it. For three days, demonstrators walked back and forth in front of the Convention Center carrying signs denouncing circumcision and calling for the protection of infants and children.

At the end of the first day when pediatricians were beginning to leave the building to board the busses that would take them to their hotels, seven men wearing the white suits with red "blood" stains on the crotch stood in front of the building with their arms and feet outstretched. I gasped and nearly fell to my knees when I saw them. The image was so powerful! Jaws dropped and flashbulbs began to go off as people photographed the courageous men who stood there, displaying their own truth.

Photo by James Loewen

The men repeated their demonstration at the end of the following day. Word obviously had gotten around because, when the men appeared again, the front of the building was crowded with pediatricians and others taking photos of the spectacle. The evidence of circumcision victims lamenting what was done to them was finally visible—and they were turning the spotlight on the perpetrators.

Brother K (standing in the center) was one of the men wearing a bloodstained suit. Brother K and his wife, Carole Anne, had worn masks and carried signs to bring attention to the issue years earlier. They had been busy raising and homeschooling their daughter. But now, Brother K was back, witnessing the first time in the United States that these outfits were on display. Brother K was so taken with the demonstration in New Orleans that he founded a non-profit organization of the same name (www.bloodstainedmen.org) that tours and demonstrates with intactivists in cities across the country. Brother K credits Jonathon for bringing the imagery to the United States.

In May 2016, Jonathon and the Bay Area Intactivists joined our demonstration on Worldwide Day of Genital Autonomy at the Ferry Building. This is always an interesting and exhilarating location because of the City's diverse inhabitants and international visitors to this famous San Francisco landmark. When Jonathon went to lunch with a group of us at a nearby restaurant after our demonstration, I shared a story with him about my friend Katie, whom I'd had the honor of welcoming into the world three decades earlier. Katie said she had seen Jonathon in Golden Gate Park, riding his bicycle adorned with a sign that said, "Forced Circumcision Violates Human Rights." She had her little son with her in her arms. Katie had informed herself and wisely chosen to protect her baby from genital cutting. She told me that when she saw Jonathon on his bicycle she felt proud of her decision and of Jonathon for spreading the word.

At the end of our lunch, I asked Jonathon if he was going to be with us at the Capitol building in Sacramento for our demonstration the following Tuesday. Jonathon said he wasn't going to make it. I told him I was sorry but that I would see him at the San Francisco Pride Parade in June. The following day, Sunday May 8, Jonathon

Photo from Jonathon Conte

made a large sign for Mother's Day, thanking mothers for protecting their sons from circumcision.

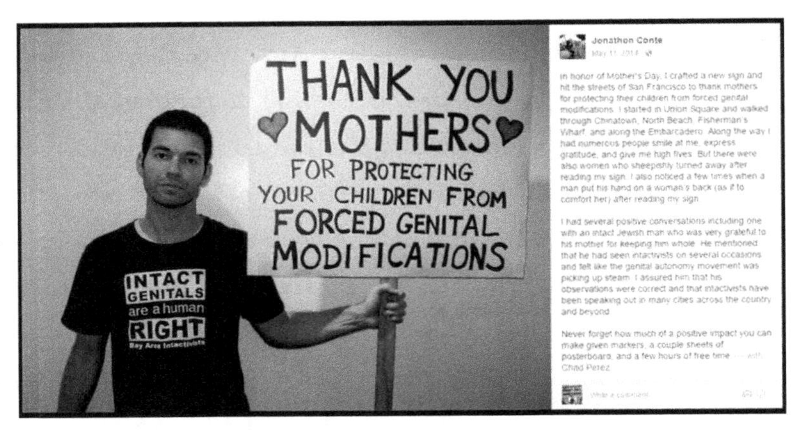

Photo from Jonathon Conte

In the wee hours of that night, I received a call from filmmaker Eliyahu Ungar-Sargon telling me the sad news that Jonathon had taken his own life. I burst into tears. My first thought was that this tormented young man finally had peace. His parents had not accepted his body as it was when he was born so they had him circumcised. They didn't accept him again when they realized he was gay and sent him to religious conversion therapy camp every summer when he was in high school. When he finally had the courage to tell his mother he disliked being circumcised, she told him to "get over it."

Photo from Jonathon Conte

We need circumcised men to speak about their feelings so that expectant parents hear how our ignorant or coerced decisions affect our sons and daughters. So many men living with the consequences of foreskin amputation have been laughed out of psychologists' offices or told to "get over it." It is impossible to get over a primal wound. The best we can do is understand what has caused the pain, prevent the infliction of the same wounds on others, and hope to find solace and satisfaction from our work.

We celebrate Jonathon's life every year following our Worldwide Day of Genital Autonomy Demonstration with our Jonathon Conte Memorial Luncheon. I would prefer his presence in life, but in death he has become a martyr for the cause he so eloquently championed.

Chapter 23

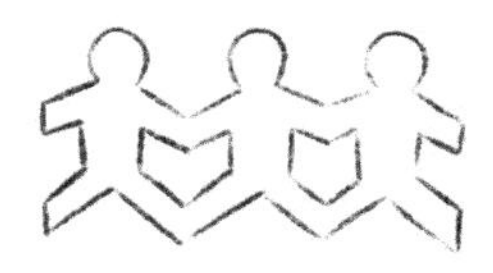

LEGAL BREAKDOWNS, A TRAGIC LEGAL VICTORY, AND AN UNEXPECTED BREAKTHROUGH

I would not normally volunteer for a trip to Fargo, North Dakota, in subzero weather. But in February 2003, a group of intactivists from around the country went to the Flatt vs. Kantak trial to support the cause of bodily integrity for both males and females and the right to informed consent regarding circumcision. We were kindly welcomed at a local bed and breakfast, where our time was made bearable despite the brutal weather and the legal shenanigans we were compelled to witness in the courtroom.

The case had first been brought in December 1999 by James and Anita Flatt on behalf of their infant son Josiah. The couple contended that Dr. Sunita Kantak of Fargo's MeritCare Hospital failed to inform them of the risks and benefits of circumcision prior to performing the surgery on their infant son Josiah, born March 6, 1997.[59] In addition, the Flatts were also suing the State of North Dakota, alleging that N.D.C.C. §12.1-36-01, the female genital mutilation law, violated the equal protection provisions of the federal and state constitutions. The lawsuit against the state was dismissed in 2000. The lawsuit against Dr. Kantak went to trial by jury in February 2003, which was why we were there.

This was a rather unusual case as there was no claim of injury during the circumcision process. But I hoped it would be educational for the courts regarding what I deem the ever-so-important provision of accurate information prior to the signing of an informed consent for circumcision.

The Flatt's attorney, Zenas Baer, said that the consent form Anita Flatt was asked to sign did not offer enough information on circumcision to constitute informed consent, and that she had been asked to sign the form the night of the birth, when she was on medication for pain. Dr. Kantak, who was to perform the circumcision, spoke briefly with Anita the next day, but Anita said that he did not discuss circumcision in any detail.

Attorney Baer was not allowed to show the jurors a circumcision video, surgical instruments, or a Circumstraint; all of these exhibits would have been critical for a parent, jury, or reasonable person to make a truly informed decision about whether to allow the permanent removal of a part of a baby's penis. This was judicial censorship. Pathologist Christopher Cold was not allowed to use slides to explain what the foreskin is and what is lost with its amputation. Instead, he had to draw illustrations during his testimony. All this did was reinforce the lack of information available to a parent because existing brochures or printed information given to parents about circumcision typically do not include a video, a picture of surgical instruments and a Circumstraint, or an explanation of the foreskin and what is lost with circumcision.

At one point, experts from both sides agreed that "for an elective procedure such as circumcision, all risks, no matter how small, should be disclosed to the patient or the patient's guardian." Despite this agreement, the judge instructed the jury that a doctor must inform a patient only of serious and likely risks.[60] If the first premise is true how can the judge's instruction, diametrically opposed to disclosing all risks, be valid?

Defense "experts," including two members of the 1999 American Academy of Pediatrics (AAP) Task Force Committee on Circumcision, claimed that no one knows the function of the foreskin. Attorney Baer asked, **"So, doctors cut off a part of the body without knowing its functions?"**

I wanted to jump up and quote the passage that Ed Wallerstein had written for the 1984 original, misspelled AAP brochure on *Care of the Uncircumcized [sic] Penis*—which, under the heading of "The Function of the Foreskin," clearly defined the function of the foreskin. So, this was the result of the AAP sticking its head in a hole and refusing to include that information in their revised brochure. Physicians do not know, or ignore, that **the function of the foreskin is to shield the glans from infection throughout life and to enhance sexual function and sensation.**

These same physicians, who were each paid thousands of dollars by attorneys to testify, also claimed that baby Josiah was not injured when his foreskin was amputated.

That wasn't what was under consideration at this trial. But I noted to myself that it depends on where you are born and live, and what your values are, as to whether a baby boy is injured when his foreskin is amputated. I happen to understand, after decades of study and discussion, that the intact penis is a normal penis, and to remove the foreskin is an injury.

Dr. Kantak, the obstetrician who circumcised Anita's baby, and hospital nurses called as witnesses claimed babies never scream during circumcision. Some "even sleep" through the surgery, they said—obviously not understanding that those babies who appear to sleep have gone into shock from pain and are in a semi-comatose state.

Even with obvious unreasonable and irrational obstacles placed before him to keep truthful facts out of the discussion, attorney Baer did an exemplary job. In his closing argument, he reviewed the foreskin's benefits and the risks and harms from circumcision. He asked jurors, "What would a reasonable person want to know to make a decision as to whether circumcision is in the 'best interest of their child'?" *A lot more than this court was willing to let experts reveal or jurors know,* I thought to myself, since jurors were prevented from fully understanding what a circumcision involves and how it affects a newborn.

The jury—selected from a pool of 28 prospective jurors that included 12 employees of a medical institution or who had a spouse that was—deliberated for just two-and-a-half hours and came back with an ignorance- or allegiance-revealing verdict of *not guilty* for circumciser Kantak and the hospital.

It's worth noting that a London filmmaker had spent two weeks in North Dakota earlier in 2003 working on a documentary about the high rate of circumcision—85 to 95 percent—in the U.S. Midwest. Compared to the United Kingdom, where fewer than five percent of boys are circumcised, these rates are astonishing and reveal the pathology of the U.S. circumcising culture.[61]

Daily media coverage on every television station and in the local newspapers during the two-week trial included the words *amputation, erogenous tissue,* and other informative adjectives. Hopefully, education had been initiated in North Dakota.

● ● ●

Jacob Sweet, a young man who spent his life in a wheelchair unable to do the least thing for himself, died in 2012. What happened to him? He was a victim of an unnecessary circumcision.[62]

Jacob was born a healthy and normal baby on January 16, 1986. His health deteriorated after he was circumcised the day after his birth by James Nesbitt, MD, of the Children's Clinic at Providence Hospital in Anchorage, Alaska. On January 25, Jacob's parents, Gary and Beverly Sweet, brought him to the Emergency Room at Providence because he was vomiting and fussy and the circumcision site was red and swollen, indicating an infection.

Daniel Tulip, MD, admitted Jacob to the hospital, after which he barely saw him. Even though Jacob had seizures for 24 hours, he was not seen by a neonatologist. Besides Dr. Tulip's lack of involvement, the attending nurse had turned down the alarm that indicated Jacob was about to have a seizure because it was bothering other people. In the wee hours of January 27, Jacob had a massive seizure that left him severely brain-damaged and nearly blind.

Because there were many troubling aspects to this case, the Sweets sued the hospital and treating physicians for malpractice and negligence. One of the points of the lawsuit was that the Sweets had never received information about circumcision when they signed an "informed consent" for the surgery. Beverly thought circumcision was mandatory, and none of the staff remembered informing Beverly about circumcision. Conveniently, the nursing records pertaining to Jacob's treatments went missing.

Incredibly, the jury returned a verdict in favor of the doctors and hospital, awarding $150,000 in attorney's fees to both the hospital and the physicians to be paid by the Sweets. The legal team representing the Sweets was later found to have misrepresented their expertise in malpractice, which was part of the absence of justice. They did not even present evidence by key witnesses who believed that the medical records had been intentionally destroyed.

It was particularly galling to me to know that Dr. Thomas Wiswell (whom I had tried very hard *not* to consider my nemesis despite his stand on the supposed, though debunked, benefits of circumcision) was an expert witness for the defendants, arguing that Jacob's brain damage could not have resulted from an infection from his circumcision, but was probably caused by an unknown virus. I couldn't help but wonder how much Wiswell had been paid for *that* testimony.

The Sweets did not give up and were able to retain legal and malpractice attorney Mark Johnson, who won an unnamed settlement for the family in 2000. But it took 13 years for the Sweets to get legal justice for Jacob. The settlement helped pay for Jacob's medical bills and ongoing care but could never compensate that family for what they went through as a result of an infected circumcision.

●●●

The Flatt vs Kantak trial may have been a legal fiasco. And the injury to Jacob Sweet was a tragedy. But progress was being made across the country because of NOCIRC and other organizations and individuals raising awareness of the risks of circumcision and demanding that parents receive more information.

When Lloyd Schofield invited me to lunch in San Francisco in 2009 and asked what he could do to help the movement, I wasn't sure what to suggest but said I would call him if anything came up. It wasn't long before something did.

Several Bay Area intactivists had decided to start a petition to put a resolution to ban non-therapeutic male circumcision of infants and children on the November ballot of the City and County of San Francisco. I called Lloyd to tell him about it. Not only was he willing to help, but he also became the media spokesperson for the monumental effort.

First, lots of signatures needed to be collected as a show of support. On April 26, 2011, I was invited by Lloyd and the Bay Area Intactivists to join them in San Francisco for the submission of several large boxes of signed petitions to put their resolution on the November ballot. These hard-working volunteers had collected several thousand more signatures than needed just in case some were duplicates or ineligible signatures. After a short waiting period, the authorities confirmed they had received enough signatures to include the resolution on the ballot.

Our celebratory mood was soon dashed by backlash from the Jewish community, the Anti-Defamation League, and the ACLU of Northern California who also brought in Muslim groups to help counter the initiative. They filed a lawsuit against the resolution's inclusion on the ballot.

On July 28, we went to the Civic Center Courthouse for the case to be heard. As we walked down the hall to the courtroom, John Geisheker, Director of Doctors Opposing Circumcision, said to me, "It feels like we're goats on our way to be slaughtered." We had no quarrel with Muslims or Jews. If their religions insisted on subjecting male children to an anachronistic blood ritual that had been practiced for millenia, there wasn't much anyone else could do to change that thinking. But, as evidenced by the number of signatures collected for supporting the ballot measure, it was time for the people of San Francisco to decide whether *all children*, regardless of the religious or cultural beliefs of their parents, should have legal protection from unnecessary genital surgery.

In the courtroom, three male Jewish attorneys from New York and one tall, female Muslim attorney from San Jose, California, stood up to argue for religious freedom as a rationale for child circumcision. *But what does that mean?* It seemed to me that when a child's body is labeled as Muslim or Jewish, his constitutional right to religious freedom has already been violated and denied. Michael Kinane, our pro-bono attorney, bravely stood up to defend the right of every child to bodily integrity and genital autonomy, that is, personal choice about what body parts they may want to keep.

Using a law that prohibits local governments from regulating medical practice—*a law passed to allow veterinarians to declaw cats without medical reason*—Superior Court Judge Loretta Giorgi struck the measure from the ballot. Thousands of San Franciscans had signed the petition for a right to vote on the matter but were denied their voice and their vote. After the hearing, those of us who had worked so hard to collect signatures and promote the facts underlying the proposed ballot measure were all astonished by the court's unwillingness to uphold the will of the people to vote on a matter that potentially affects every child born in San Francisco.

We walked outside the courthouse and across the street to where Lloyd was being interviewed by Brendon Marotta for inclusion in Brendon's documentary, *American Circumcision.* I saw a man wearing a yarmulke listening to the interview. When he looked in my direction, I smiled and said, "Listening in?" He responded with a smile. I asked if I could give him the NOCIRC pamphlet on the *Bioethics of Circumcision*. He graciously took it and thanked me, saying he appreciated it. He obviously was curious, thoughtful, and kind.

As this friendly man and I chatted, Brian Levitt came up to us. Brian was wearing a bright blue T-shirt with a large white Star of David across the chest. He carried two signs: one proclaimed infants' rights, the other testified to his being a Jew against circumcision. Brian began telling the man with the yarmulke how upset and angry he is that his parents and his tribe allowed someone to cut off a normal part of his penis. "As a gay man," he said, "I have seen intact males have an orgasm and I know that I will never be able to have that experience because a mohel cut off my foreskin without my consent!"

The man identified himself by saying, "I am Irwin Kula, a seventh-generation rabbi. I have never heard anyone say anything like that before. However, if you're telling me this, I had better listen." And listen he did. I had seen Brian's reaction to those who would not listen to him as he expressed his feelings and knew he could become quite distraught. During this amazing conversation, I watched Brian as he relaxed more and more. For the first time in his life, a rabbi was *listening* to him, *hearing* him, and *honoring* his experience and his feelings.

I asked Rabbi Kula if he had ever heard of *brit shalom*—a peaceful Jewish welcoming and naming ceremony that could be substituted for ritual Jewish circumcision. He had not, so I asked if he would be willing to have his name on a list of rabbis who are willing to lead this ceremony. He took the name and contact information of Dr. Mark Reiss, the Jewish physician who founded the Brit Shalom Celebrants list, now called the Inclusion Directory.[63] From our chance encounter after a bitter defeat, Rabbi Kula's name was added to that list. Sharing our stories is key to changing minds.

Chapter 24

GENITAL INTEGRITY AND GENITAL AUTONOMY

The origin of Genital Integrity Awareness Week (GIAW) stemmed from early activism by David Wilson, a man who began driving from Cocoa Beach, Florida, to Washington, D.C., in the early 1990s to protest circumcision. April is Child Abuse Protection Month—but David's initial one-man demonstration was held on April Fool's Day to make the point that the American public had been "fooled" into circumcising their sons. Although his intention was to attract attention to the cause, he understood this was a deadly serious subject.

After he acquired a computer, David found out he was not the only one who felt betrayed by the medical establishment, our culture, and our parents. He was soon joined by another Florida activist, Van Lewis, who had made history with his brother Ben when they were arrested on December 17, 1970 (nine years before my awakening!), for demonstrating against male genital cutting at the Tallahassee Memorial Hospital.

Years after Van's and David's demonstrations, the International Coalition for Genital Integrity (ICGI) launched Genital Integrity Awareness Week, April 1 to 7, 2001. The week's events began with a NOCIRC conference, Genital Integrity: A New Awareness (March 31-April 1), at the Holiday Inn in Tyson's Corner, McLean, Virginia. With NOCIRC's support, more than a hundred people from various human rights organizations, signs in hand, joined David Wilson and his Stop Infant Circumcision Society at the White House to help bolster the message he had been delivering by himself for years. With a police escort, we walked from there to the Capitol, where David directed people with large signs to help position them on the steps. James Loewen was there to capture the event with his wonderful photographs. David has come back every year for this powerful event, except during the Pandemic, and has met with hundreds of tourists, politicians, school groups, and policy makers on the Capitol's West Lawn.

Photo by James Loewen

Steven Svoboda, David Llewellyn, Marilyn Milos, and Steve Scott
(Photo by James Loewen)

For our 2001 event, Amber Craig, director of NOCIRC of North Carolina, brought copies of an International Coalition of Genital Integrity report titled *Tax Dollar Funding of Medically Unnecessary Circumcision Through Medicaid,* that she, Rio Cruz, director of ICGI, and others had diligently researched state by state. This comprehensive report revealed that more than $35 million in state and federal Medicaid dollars was being spent annually on unnecessary circumcisions. State Medicaid programs that reimburse doctors more than $50 to perform a circumcision reported a circumcision rate nearly double of that in states reimbursing less than $50. On April 2, we delivered the report to the offices of every member of Congress, along with a petition signed by the directors of 47 human rights and genital integrity organizations, asking the government to stop using federal tax dollars for medically unnecessary circumcision. (It should be noted that the dollars spent on circumcision have increased over the past 20 years.)

When intactivists returned to Washington, D.C., in April 2003 for Genital Integrity Awareness Week, NOCIRC and its state affiliates co-sponsored a week-long Intactivist Summit. Our march from the Washington Monument to the Capitol was led by William Stowell, who had spoken at our 2002 Georgetown symposium about the lawsuit he initiated at age 18 against the doctor who had circumcised him and the hospital where it occurred. The case was settled out of court in William's favor, but it did not provide us with a legal precedent because there was no judicial decision. At this event, William's wife Amanda also made history by going into labor after the parade and delivering their daughter, Ariana.

This was the first gathering attended by Georganne Chapin, then CEO of Hudson Health Plan, a nonprofit Medicaid HMO in New York state. Georganne quickly became my friend and fellow warrior and now leads the largest nationally recognized professionally managed nonprofit organization working to end circumcision in the world, Intact America, in the fight to end child genital cutting.

Following our educational visits to the offices of our Representatives in Washington, the states of Arizona, Missouri, North Carolina, Montana, and Utah joined California, Mississippi, Nevada, North Dakota, Oregon, and Washington state in eliminating Medicaid funding of circumcision. Florida, Maine, and Utah were soon to follow.

• • •

The more I learned about the unethical imposition of circumcision on males in the United States and a child's inviolable right to genital integrity, the easier it was to join forces with those opposing any medically unnecessary genital alterations, including forced or coerced circumcision of adults, and the surgical alterations performed on the genitals of children born with ambiguous genitalia (one of several conditions now referred to as "intersex") prior to the age of consent.

The conundrum of what to do when an infant is born with genitalia not definitively either male or female was impressed upon me in a riveting presentation at NOCIRC's 7th symposium, in 2002, at Georgetown University in Washington, D.C. The presenter, Milton Diamond, was a professor at the John A. Burns School of Medicine at the University of Hawaii. He also was host and co-producer of the PBS TV series *Human Sexuality*, which discussed management of "intersex" children born with ambiguous genitalia. The standard practice in hospitals until the late 1990s had been for physicians to "decide" the gender of such children. For example, for a child who might be biologically male but had a very small penis that would be surgically difficult for doctors to fabricate into a functional penis, this could mean removing the small external organ and raising this boy as a girl. In the case of a girl with an "enlarged" clitoris, a physician would typically reduce its size by cutting a part off. Once these infants and children grew up, they often lamented the choice adults had made for them, the surgeries they had suffered and endured throughout their childhood, and the secrecy and shame with which they lived. They would have preferred to have kept *every* part of their genitals and to have their male and female attributes acknowledged, accepted, and preserved until they could make their own decisions.

Diamond was instrumental in exposing the tragic story of Canadian twin boys born in 1965.[64] The first twin, David Reimer, was circumcised at eight months after being inaccurately diagnosed with phimosis, a non-retractable foreskin, that is normal in male infants and children. Some doctors today still believe the attachment of the foreskin to the glans in infancy and childhood is pathologic. *It is not!* Phimosis is a physiological condition that is a normal part of penile development and normal in a small number of males who have non-problematic phimosis throughout life. David's circumcision was performed using an electrocautery device rather than a scalpel to amputate his foreskin. The device came into contact with the metal Gomco clamp on the baby's penis, electrifying the clamp and literally frying David's penis. The circumcision was canceled for the second twin, allowing him to grow up with an intact penis that was left to retract normally—which it did.

At the time of this surgical catastrophe, John Money, a New Zealand psychologist and sex researcher on the faculty of Johns Hopkins University, was working with children born with ambiguous genitalia. He said that genitals and gender could be altered if children were nurtured to grow up as one gender or the other. Thus, children born with ambiguous genitalia often underwent surgeries to make them fit into our male or female binary gender system.

David's parents heard about Money's work and took David to be examined by him. David would be Money's first developmentally normal boy, that is, a child born clearly male, whose penis had been destroyed in a medical accident. David's parents were told by Money—who was thrilled by the opportunity to compare identical twins with one as a control and one as an experiment—to raise David as a "girl."

Not surprisingly, this attempt to overcome Mother Nature's design failed. As I wrote to Dr. Money, I did not think any amount of nurturing could or would alter nature or the Y chromosome present in every cell of a male's body. The tragic results became apparent when David Reimer appeared on *The Oprah Winfrey Show* on February 9, 2000, hoping his story would spare others the same suffering. Not long after that appearance, David took his own life, preceded by his brother who had also been deeply affected by his twin's tragic life. Their story was documented first in *Rolling Stone* magazine in December 1987, and then in John Colapinto's book, *As Nature Made Him: The Boy Who Was Raised as a Girl*.[65]

The 13th International Symposium on Genital Autonomy and Children's Rights, held in July 2014 at the University of Colorado, Boulder, featured an introduction to the pioneers of the Genital Autonomy Movement for the benefit of our newcomers. In addition, we offered two screenings of a groundbreaking documentary, *Intersexion,* a film that demystifies a variety of conditions formerly known as hermaphroditism. The movie explores how intersex people navigate their lives when their bodies don't fit the binary model of male or female.[66]

In some societies, intersex people are revered because they don't sit on either side of the gender divide. These cultures understand male and female genders as being at each end of a spectrum and acknowledge that we *all* have male and female attributes somewhere along that spectrum. However, in the United States and other developed countries, historically, teams of doctors and psychologists, along with the child's parents—who face an agonizing decision—will decide which gender to assign to the child. Thankfully, due to activism, this approach is no longer the norm.[67]

In Boulder, Hida Viloria, an advocate for intersex people who was born with both XX and XY chromosomes, so intersex herself, and an advocate for intersex people, gave a talk called "'Normalizing' Genital Surgeries of Intersex Children." Hida has a degree in Gender and

Sexuality from UC Berkeley. She is Chairperson of OII, Organisation of Intersex International, the world's largest intersex advocacy organization, and Director of its American affiliate, OII-USA. On December 10, 2013, she became the first openly intersex person to speak, with Martina Navratilova and others, at the annual United Nations Human Rights Day event commemorating the anniversary of the 1948 adoption of the Universal Declaration of Human Rights.

Hida spoke about being raised female, which is why she is comfortable with feminine pronouns. As a child, she was never told she also had male attributes. Fortunately, she was protected from "corrective" surgery after birth by her physician father. As a college student in Berkeley, she read an article titled "Born Neither" and wondered if the condition prompting the article might have something to do with her own differences. Several people had mentioned to Hida that she was "different," but she didn't understand how or why. She had herself tested and learned she has both XX and XY chromosomes. After discovering she had a Y chromosome in every cell of her body, Hida realized she could no longer accurately call herself a lesbian.

Hida learned about the physical and psychological consequences of genital surgeries when she attended the first gathering of intersex people in California. She went to the event thinking she would meet people with varying physical attributes and learn how they lived with their differences. Instead, the participants talked about having lived through childhoods that consisted of surgeries, secrecy, and shame. Horrified by the stories she heard and, as an intersex person who had been left intact, Hida felt an obligation to make a difference in the world—to help others understand that intersex people are not to be feared, surgically altered, or obliterated. I was deeply moved by this courageous, intelligent, articulate human rights activist with a crucially important message about human rights.

When I left the auditorium for lunch, I was accompanied by Leonid Dunn, who had come from Liberia to talk about his work to end female genital mutilation in his country. Just before coming to America, a Liberian newspaper published an article about Leonid's organization and the work it was doing to end FGM. Immediately following publication, the lives of Leonid and his three colleagues were threatened. All four activists escaped to Sierra Leone and then came to the United States. Fearing for their lives, they filed for asylum and have been awaiting determination ever since. As we walked to the cafeteria, Leonid looked at me and said, "There are no intersex people in Liberia." When I asked why, he said, "Because it is more embarrassing to have an intersex baby than to have a dead baby."

When Sheila Curran and I wrote the papers for our NOCIRC nonprofit status in 1985, our stated purpose for the organization was to provide information to educate parents, healthcare professionals, and others about routine circumcision. Our first pamphlet, *Answers to Your Questions about NOCIRC*, said our organization is dedicated to "securing the birthright of male, female, and intersex infants and children to keep their sex organs intact." It seems that even then, we knew the universality of our cause.

NOCIRC Centers were formed worldwide to educate people locally. Other organizations with similar missions followed NOCIRC's lead: Doctors Opposing Circumcision, Nurses for the Rights of the Child, Attorneys for the Rights of the Child, the International Coalition for

Genital Integrity, the National Organization to Halt the Abuse and Routine Mutilation of Males (NOHARMM), the National Organization of Restoring Men (NORM), NORM-UK, Bay Area Intactivists, and more.

The movement was growing, and I felt it was important to acknowledge this, as well as to explicitly include evolving and new perspectives. At our symposium at Keele University in England in 2008, the term "Genital Autonomy" was conceived by Paul Mason, an Australian who was at the time serving as Commissioner for Children in Tasmania. Paul recognized the power of the International Child for Genital Autonomy, the logo of our symposium, and the need to protect all children worldwide. David Smith founded Genital Autonomy (GA) in the UK that same year as an umbrella organization for an international effort and adopted the International Child logo. In January 2016, I, along with the NOCIRC Board of Directors, decided to affiliate with GA, and to adopt the name "Genital Autonomy-America." GA-Finland, GA-Canada, and the Australasian Institute for Genital Autonomy are, like GA-America, offshoots of the original international charity registered in the UK. We had moved from saying "No to circumcision" to saying "Yes to intact genitals." The phrase "genital autonomy" emphasizes personal choice and that no one but the person who owns their body has the right to make decisions about their genitals.

I worried for two years prior to the name change about what to do regarding the NOCIRC Centers. Several were using our non-profit status to receive non-profit organization rates for booths at baby fairs, and they used our NOCIRC pamphlets, newsletters, and CDs as their handouts. The same day I sent a letter to each of the Centers announcing the name change, Georganne Chapin told me about a new organization, Your Whole Baby, founded by Jen Williams in Texas. I looked on the YWB website, liked what I saw, and contacted Jen to ask if she would be willing to welcome NOCIRC members into her organization. Jen was doing community outreach and creating educational products. She was in the process of acquiring 501(c)(3) non-profit status and happy to welcome anyone who wanted to join her organization. She was doing the work I wished I'd had time to do. I sent a follow-up letter to NOCIRC Center Directors the next day telling them they would be able to join Jen and carry on with their work under the Your Whole Baby banner. I was relieved and deeply grateful. As had happened so many times over the years, my hopes and dreams continued to be fueled by like-minded people dedicated to protecting the health of babies.

Chapter 25

HIGHLIGHTS FROM SYMPOSIA OVER THE YEARS

At NOCIRC's 6th symposium, in Sydney, Australia, in 2000, attendees were shocked to learn that the rate of circumcision in South Korea had gone from less than one percent to close to 100 percent in the span of fifty years.[68] What could be the cause of this in a country with strong Confucian and Buddhist traditions that had long valued preserving the body as a gift?[69] If you said, "the influence of the United States during the Korean War," you are right. By 2000, the rate of circumcision for South Korean high school boys exceeded 90 percent, which was even greater than that in the U.S.

Professor DaiSik Kim, PhD, Associate Professor of Physics at Seoul National University, came to my office months before our symposium to discuss the high rate of circumcision in South Korea. When I heard about the situation, I invited him to speak at our symposium, and told him I would honor him with a Human Rights Award with the hope of bringing media attention to the problem in his country. He contacted newspapers in South Korea prior to the symposium, but he and the award were never mentioned. When he returned from the symposium to South Korea after the media office at his university printed news of the award, other media outlets across the country picked up the story.

That was the beginning of a very successful anti-circumcision campaign in South Korea.

In 2002, I received a book from Myung-Geol, DaiSik Kim's co-presenter at the symposium, which has two drawings on the front cover—the first, a half-peeled banana and the second, an unpeeled banana. I can read just one word of the book—NOCIRC, which is on the front cover. I couldn't help feeling proud and grateful that our message was now being heard in South Korea—and making a difference. Still, I was appalled at the unconscionable role the U.S. had played in turning a culturally conscientious non-circumcising country into a circumcising country.

●●●

Dean Edell provided a new and exciting opportunity for me to be involved with hands-on research that I would present at our 9th International Symposium in 2006 at the University of Washington in Seattle. He said he would donate a Semmes-Weinstein testing kit with touch-test monofilaments to determine neurological responses of the hands and feet to calibrated stimuli to NOCIRC if I would use it to conduct a study to test penile sensitivity in adult males. Although the process of getting the testing approved and accredited was more complicated than I thought it would be, I was happy to add my name to a research study, expanding my skill set from educator and activist to author of a scientific article.

Retired pediatrician Dr. Morrie Sorrells agreed to help with the research. Leland Tremain, a Nurse Practitioner and founder of Rainbow Flag Health Services, was happy to let us use his office in Oakland on weekends for our research and offered his assistance. I asked statistician and UC Berkeley doctoral student, Tina Kimmel, MSW, MPH, and now PhD, if she would be interested in crunching the numbers. Sheila and I began recruiting both circumcised and intact males for our study, and our research began.

The monofilaments used for our testing looked like a toothbrush with a single bristle. Each monofilament varied in thickness and was calibrated to determine the pressure needed for the filament to bend. This meant that our calibrated findings were repeatable. For our study, we began by touching a specific spot on the penis with the thinnest filament and worked up to the filament first felt by the participant. We recorded the pressure, using the numbers printed on the handle of each filament.

The reason for our mapping penile sensitivity was to prove the obvious—when tens of thousands of specialized erogenous nerve endings encircling the opening of the foreskin and the part of the penis that glides back and forth over the glans during sexual activity are amputated, sexual sensations are dramatically diminished. When the protective covering of the glans is amputated, the mucosal tissue that covers the glans loses its moisture and sensitivity and the tissue becomes calloused to protect itself from chafing caused by clothing, towels, bed linens, etc.

During that study, which we ended up calling our "pilot" study, we had an opportunity to test several subjects twice to be sure our results were accurate and repeatable. We learned that the temperature in the room was a significant factor in subject responses. When the room was a little warmer, subjects were more responsive to the monofilaments. Interestingly, the results of the places on the penis we tested didn't change with temperature in relation to one another. That is, the places that were most sensitive still were, no matter the temperature of the room; and the places with the least sensitivity still were less responsive. The entire penis sensitivity changed evenly with room temperature. After recognizing the variation in response with temperature, we regulated and monitored room temperature.

Discussing our work with UC Berkeley colleagues, Tina learned that Institutional Review Board approval was required for human research if a study was to get published. Tina applied for approval from the UC Berkeley's Committee for the Protection of Human Subjects. However, the Board required a million-dollar insurance policy on each of the Regents of UC Berkeley. We could not provide that.

Next, we contacted the Western Institutional Review Board in Washington state and submitted our application for research approval. They denied approval twice. Frustrated, Dr. Sorrells and I made an appointment and went to their office in Washington to face the board directly to seek approval for our research work. Board members wanted to know what our research was and why we were doing it. We said we were creating a penile sensitivity map.

One doctor from South America was concerned about our research being conducted at the Rainbow Flag Health Services office. He asked what services were offered at the office. We told him it was a health clinic and sperm bank. Interestingly, Leland, the Nurse Practitioner who ran the clinic, had those receiving sperm from the bank sign a form agreeing to keep their baby intact. The doctor said, "I wouldn't feel comfortable entering such a place, so if you're going to do this research, I suggest you do it somewhere else."

The upshot of our visit with the Board was that, to get approval, we needed to find another place to do our research. We also were required to take an online human research course offered by the University of Florida.

Four doctors, two nurses, and many volunteers staffed the offices we rented in San Francisco for the follow-up to our initial pilot study. Once all our doctors and nurses had taken and passed the Florida course on human research—an interesting course about the history of establishing human rights guidelines for human study subjects in the wake of the Nuremburg trials—we began our research again.

For two weeks, we tested one man after another. We worked to get equal numbers of both intact and circumcised men. At the end of our office rental agreement, we didn't have enough recruits for the number we needed. One of the doctors and I agreed to work several weekends to complete the testing. Once done, we had 159 participants. The results were the same as the pilot study: circumcision ablates the most sensitive parts of the penis.

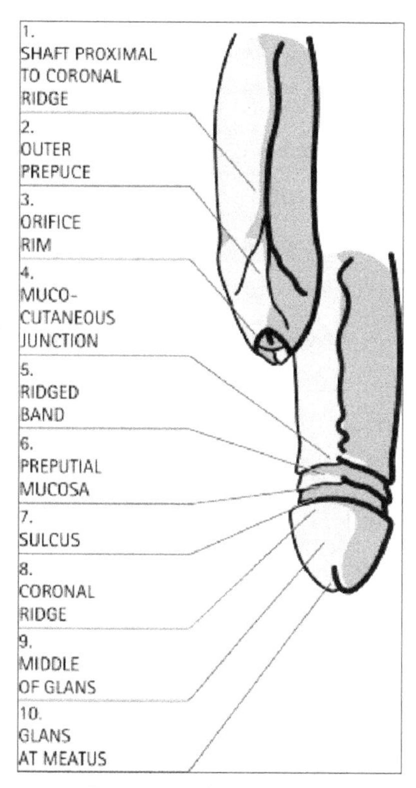

Locations on the dorsal penis.

Jeff Borg, a medical illustrator, created forms—used in both the pilot and follow-up studies—with images for us so that we could document each site that we tested and record the results of our testing.

I asked Robert Van Howe, MD, MS (Statistics), to crunch the numbers for us, which he did, along with writing up our research and our results in preparation for submission to a medical journal. Dr. Van Howe submitted our research article first to the *New England Journal of Medicine* and then to the *American Journal of Urology* to no avail. Finally, *BJU International*, a monthly peer-reviewed journal established in 1929, accepted and published our article, "Fine-Touch Pressure Thresholds in the Adult Penis."[70]

It made sense that anything an intact man felt with his foreskin was more than what a circumcised man felt without one because circumcision removed somewhere between 20,000 and 70,000 erogenous nerve endings. Since U.S. medical and social cultures have consistently denied this because there was no proof of it other than anecdotal (such as from men who had their foreskins restored), we set out to give researchers a baseline with our study so naysayers could no longer dismiss the foreskin or call it a useless piece of skin. Some doctors and hospitals threw the amputated foreskin into the trash as biological waste, and some donated it to the highest bidder as a vital asset to medical research, for example, bioengineered tissue replacement for burn victims. But perhaps its highest value is to the individual who is intact and therefore has more sensitivity to touch.

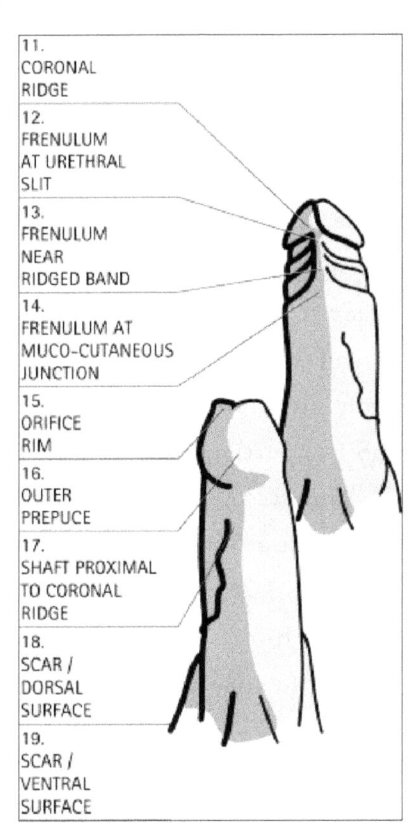

Locations on ventral penis.

•••

Eliyahu Ungar-Sargon showed his documentary *Cut: Slicing Through the Myths of Circumcision* in 2008 at the 10th international symposium at the University of Keele in Newcastle, England. His father was in attendance at the showing of this powerful film as well, which not only advocates in defense of children's rights to genital autonomy but shows how change is possible even in cases of circumcision performed as a religious ritual. In his first interview with his father in the documentary, Eliyahu asked him how he would feel if Eli chose not to have a son circumcised. Predictably, his Orthodox father said he would be upset if his grandson was not circumcised. The mohel who had circumcised Eli's grandfather had also circumcised his father, and Eli, too. Circumcision was a given, signifying the covenant between God and Abraham for centuries.

Then, halfway through the film, Eli again interviewed his father, saying that, as a neurologist, his father surely understood the baby was in pain during circumcision and that the effects of the lost erogenous nerve endings lasted a lifetime, with which his father agreed. His father now said the only reason for having Eli's son circumcised was their religion: "This is where you decide if you are Jewish or not."

Toward the end of the documentary, Eli interviewed his father one more time, asking him how he felt about Eli's position on circumcision after seeing parts of the film and listening to Eli's reasoning and evidence against circumcision. His father explained that he raised his son to be moral, ethical, and to question and challenge everything. Now he realized that, while their beliefs might be different, he had to accept his son's choices. I felt so proud when I heard him say that. I looked at his father after the film and said I felt honored to meet such a moral and ethical father. Everyone in the room stood up and applauded Eli's father. What a tribute to growth, acceptance, and love.

Something else that happened during our time in England was the presentation to several of us of silver pendants in the shape of our International Child for Genital Autonomy logo. The design was created by Ofra Pleban, a Jewish woman, as the logo for our symposia series shortly after the 1st International Symposium in 1989. I have worn mine every day since. The design represents a commitment to protect *all* children—male, female, and intersex—from non-therapeutic genital alterations. The beauty of the piece often elicits questions and comments, making it a wonderful educational opportunity.

●●●

The 11th symposium, which was held at the University of California in Berkeley in 2010, coincided with the 25th anniversary of the founding of NOCIRC. The day after the symposium, buses brought attendees from Berkeley to NOCIRC Headquarters at my home in Forest Knolls, California. People had come from Argentina, Australia, Canada, Germany, Ireland, Italy, Kenya, New Zealand, the UK, and across the United States to attend our symposium so the anniversary was observed by a wonderful international group of supporters.

A local baker made a cake; knowing my work, the decorator took it upon herself to decorate the cake with the outline of an intact penis under the words NOCIRC. While funny, I found it difficult when it came time to cut the "penis cake," and asked someone else to take on that task.

We gathered in celebration of the work we had done and were doing in the world. We had become an international family and I was sorry when our time together was over, and people climbed back into the buses. I hoped people would see that big things can happen from small beginnings.

Georganne Chapin, Pia Grassivaro Gallo, and me (Photo by James Loewen)

I felt compelled to respond to a Finnish imam attendee at our 2012 symposium, in Helsinki, Finland, when he said that circumcisions should be done where they are safe—in the hospital. I stood up and said that, as a nurse working in a hospital, I watched babies go into respiratory and cardiac arrest and saw grievous mistakes happen during hospital circumcisions. No matter where the cutting takes place or what body part is amputated, there are *always* risks.

The imam would not be swayed until Tim Hammond showed photographs from his *Harm Documentation Survey* depicting the horror of what many men have suffered because of circumcision. After the presentation, the imam approached me at the back of the room where I was standing and said, "We must do something to bring this to an end!" Perhaps the imam was better able to recognize the pain and trauma adult men were enduring from their circumcision because, as a Muslim, he doesn't have a primal wound from neonatal circumcision; he was older when he experienced that traumatic event.

●●●

I'd like to insert a note here, which is only the tip of the iceberg regarding the different personalities we have dealt with at events over the years. At each symposium there has been some kind of incident with attendees, unrelated to the content we have presented. But one particular character puzzled us all.

At the Sydney, Australia symposium, the University contacted us about a man rummaging through student lockers. Ken found our attendee with his head in a student's locker. Ken told the man, who had been allowed into the locker room to retrieve "a forgotten item," that this was not how we expected our attendees to behave, especially because his conduct reflected on all of us.

This attendee returned for the 7th symposium at Georgetown University in Washington, D.C. This time, he brought multiple plastic bags with him to fill with food from the catered lunch outside the event room, although there was no evidence of a hungry family to feed and he should have been able to fill up during lunch time. Apparently he was using this lunch to fill his belly for the entire time he was at the symposium.

He showed up at the Padua symposium without money for a place to stay. He slept outdoors until he was told he was not allowed to sleep in the park. So, he climbed over the fence of a used car lot next to the student facilities where we were staying and slept in one of the cars parked there. When we were told about his actions, Ken gave him another warning. His behavior was getting more and more worrisome *and* tiresome. As if that wasn't enough, he called me after he got home and told me he'd gotten a bicycle while he was in Italy. I asked how he could afford it and he said it was in a bicycle stand for a week with a broken pedal, so he figured it was left by someone. I said, "What if that someone was a child who was working and saving his money to buy himself a new pedal?" I told him what he did was stealing, no matter how he tried to justify it. After our conversation, I wrote him a letter telling him I was disappointed by his behavior that jeopardized us all and that his misdeeds must cease. Whatever made me think that would stop him?

He showed up yet again in Helsinki! He arrived without money and asked one of our kind doctors to let him share his room. Dr. Jim Snyder, having watched this fellow's unscrupulous escapades for so many years, went up to him upon his arrival at the symposium and told him he was not welcome and could not attend. Then, the man went on to tell everyone how I would not allow his participation. I told him that was not my way of handling things, but I had asked him again and again to mind himself and he ignored my request. I said he had dishonored himself, I no longer trusted him, and I would not argue with Jim's decision. It probably should not have taken me so long to support banning him from the symposia, but I was ever mindful of censoring people's rights. I still wonder, though, how he was able to afford registration and transportation costs when he seemed unable to pay for food and lodging.

• • •

By the 14th symposium, back at Keele University in Newcastle, I was noticing a different trend in the selection of presenters. The British contingent of Genital Autonomy seemed to be sidelining North Americans and their organizations in favor of European representatives. They believed European efforts were making a difference while the United States had maintained pro-circumcision policies. This, of course, is why we needed to continue with participation in the symposia we initiated. The idea of our exclusion was hurtful to our faithful supporters and counter to my vision of our inclusive international movement.

I had planned on this symposium being my last, but I could not in good conscience end on such a negative note. Not only had the symposium been exclusionary, but it was also the most poorly attended of all the prior symposia, with 67 participants, 26 of them presenters. I trust our Europeans friends will lead the way in ending genital cutting of non-consenting minors in their countries, and I offer them my gratitude and appreciation. But I felt compelled to recapture the inviting and welcoming positive environment of our earlier symposia by organizing one more gathering—on my turf, where I knew I could count on both our faithful supporters over the decades and all the newly aware anti-violence adherents of preserving the child's natural body. Aside from a few isolated outposts, like the nurses of St. Vincent Hospital in Santa Fe, the San Francisco Bay Area was ground zero for educating the public about the risks of an unnecessary surgery performed routinely on infants.

I held my final and the 15th International Symposium on Genital Autonomy and Children's Rights in 2018. We returned to the same venue as our second symposium, only the name of the hotel had changed from the Myako to the Kabuki Hotel. Many people understood this would be the last symposium I would organize and wanted to help. Presenters and participants came from Australia, Belgium, Canada, England, Germany, Israel, Japan, Liberia, Northern Ireland, and many states from within the U.S. to this celebratory event. There were more young, educated, concerned, and dedicated intactivists at this symposium than we'd ever had before, and this gave us all—especially the elders and *me*—immense hope.

Hida Viloria began the talks with her presentation, "What If We Were Free and Whole? Genital Autonomy's Transformative Impact." *Yes, what if children weren't forced to undergo unnecessary genital cutting? What if they weren't traumatized by excruciating pain at the beginning of life? What would our children and our society be like without the imprinting of sexual violence on the psyches of our infants and children?*

At the end of our second day, Brendon Marotta showed his award-winning documentary, *American Circumcision*. The film documented the growth of our movement over four decades. People across the country were demonstrating now with the same passion, dedication, and determination that I had when I first began. Brendon also gave screen time to those promoting circumcision and their less than convincing arguments. It was obvious, however, that those protecting children had the ethical rights of the child at the forefront of their argument and agenda. This was an incredible and immensely rewarding experience for me. Brendon's documentary gave us hope and is still a must-see.

The last night of the symposium, my daughter Kate, son Troy, and grandson Matthew, who had been to the first symposium when he was 12, and his wife Ella came to the podium and shared stories about me.

Kate mentioned that, when she was in her teens and her friends were borrowing their parents' cars, she and her brothers never asked to borrow mine because it had all those NOCIRC stickers on it. Then, Kate presented me with a statue of Quan Yin, the Goddess of Mercy and Compassion, also known as "She who hears all sounds of suffering in the world." When I get weary, I look at the Goddess and she helps.

At the banquet, once the music began, Troy asked me to dance. Having planned my last symposium, I knew I would be bone-tired, weary, and worn out tomorrow. But that night, I danced and danced.

Chapter 26

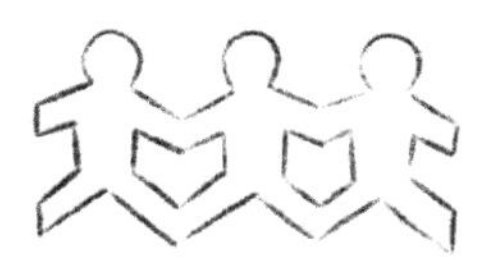

THE CIRCUMCISION CRISIS IN AFRICA

We featured sessions on Female Genital Mutilation (FGM) in our symposia almost from the beginning. The main countries in Africa where this was practiced included Djibouti, Egypt, Guinea, Mali, Somalia, Eritrea, Ethiopia, and Burkina Faso.[71] It took several more years before we began to realize the damage that was being done to African men and boys due to the insistence by some very influential Americans that circumcision would stop Africa's plague of AIDS and HIV.

At our 11th symposium in 2010 at the University of California, Berkeley, researcher David Gisselquist told attendees that unsafe healthcare practices were contributing significantly to the AIDS pandemic in Africa. However, the National Institute of Health, Centers for Disease Control and Prevention, USAID, the United Nations, and the World Health Organization stigmatize HIV-positive African men and women by claiming, against consistent evidence, that almost all HIV infections in African adults are caused by sex. Sexual behavior in Africa is no different than in Europe or the U.S., Gisselquist pointed out. What is different is that Africans are exposed to contaminated blood on instruments reused without sterilization in hospitals, during surgeries, tattooing, male and female circumcision, and blood tests.[72]

A prime example of healthcare contamination, Gisselquist noted, is the number of HIV-negative mothers with HIV-positive babies. How did babies become infected when their mothers weren't? They are vaccinated with unsterilized needles previously used to vaccinate other babies. Blaming Africa's HIV epidemic on sex when many infections come from health care encourages people to distrust spouses and needlessly destroys families.

Also addressing AIDS in Africa, Charles Geshekter, Professor Emeritus of African History at California State University, and a member of the South African Presidential AIDS Advisory Panel (2000-03), challenged the claim that African AIDS can be controlled through sexual behavior modification, male circumcision, or drugs. Three groundbreaking studies had been done in 2003 that found that two-thirds of African HIV cases were the result of contaminated medical instruments and one-third from risky sexual practices.[73]

Today, Africa is perhaps the most concerning region in the world regarding circumcision. In 2009, Microsoft founder Bill Gates gave $50 million toward a five-year program to circumcise up to 650,000 men in Swaziland and Zambia to curb HIV and AIDS. At least one of the organizations providing technical support admitted that "circumcision can't alone protect men or women against HIV, and that circumcised men should still take additional precautions, such as wearing condoms and not engaging in risky or promiscuous sex."[74]

Geshekter, speaking at our symposium, pointed out that the money being poured into circumcising African men would be better spent on poverty relief, job creation, the provision of sanitation, clean drinking water, and aid for drought-stricken farmers. Because of the research and exchange of information NOCIRC had fostered through our symposia, our expert presenters could see the flaws in the assumptions of organizations relying on biased studies that produced conclusions taken out of context. It reminded me of the early years of U.S. research on sexually transmitted infections concluding that the rate of STIs was lower among the Jewish people because they were circumcised rather than that they lived in close communities that frowned on sex outside of marriage.

Regarding our ongoing concerns about misinformation on circumcision in Africa, I want to make special note of the role of our friend Prince Hillary Maloba, who has worked tirelessly to defend the rights of the intact men in Kenya and Uganda and to condemn forced circumcision. His personal story is fascinating on its own as he comes from a royal family that ruled across western Kenya and eastern Uganda in the 18th century. Born in Uganda, his family fled to Kenya when the war toppled Idi Amin from power. At the age of nine, he was told by his father that he owed a debt to his community that required cutting off his foreskin as a sacrifice. He participated in the ritual with other boys, suffering severe pain and excessive bleeding.

Primed to protect boys and men from circumcision, Prince Hillary Maloba came upon my writings in the early 1990s and contacted me. He eventually became director of NOCIRC in Kenya and has kept us updated on the situation in Uganda and Kenya that has resulted from Western circumcision propaganda.

How does Prince Hillary Maloba know it is propaganda? His mother's brothers were among the first to die of AIDS—yet they were circumcised. He observed that Uganda was doing well in reducing HIV infections with a strategy called ABC (Abstain, Be faithful, use a Condom). After a media blitz claiming that Western scientists found that a circumcised person was 60 percent less likely to get HIV, governments in African countries began forcing uncircumcised communities to circumcise their men to end HIV/AIDS. (The "60 percent" claim has been adopted by mainstream media and repeated over and over, with no mention that it refers to relative rather than absolute risk. The difference can be illustrated as follows: If, say, ten in a thousand intact men will be infected with HIV from a sexual encounter with an HIV positive partner, four in a thousand circumcised men might be infected.)

I highlighted the problems with the international health community's obsession with circumcising African men in my 2013 NOCIRC newsletter. The publication featured a roundup of news from the Prince including observations that the highest HIV/AIDS rates come from circumcising rather than non-circumcising communities. One of the reasons for this is that those who have been circumcised believe they are protected and stop using condoms. In June 2012, he reported that more than 30 men were chased, beaten, circumcised, and dumped in the street in eastern Uganda.

This campaign of terror and misinformation must not be our legacy in Africa.

Photo sent to me by Prince Hillary Maloba

NOT THE END

Chapter 27

THE BIRTH OF INTACT AMERICA

During the early years of my quest to stop circumcision, I had volunteer help and a shoestring budget from my weekend job at a retirement home. Occasionally, as with Ralph Ginzburg and Laurence Rockefeller, an individual donor with means and a deeply personal interest in our issue would come forward with a substantial donation.

In 2007, Dean Pisani, a Texas businessman, had concerns about the ethics of infant circumcision that arose during his wife's pregnancy with their first child. After researching circumcision, he and his wife decided to keep their son intact. Although their decision was firm, while in the hospital one nurse after another asked them if their baby was going to be circumcised. Troubled by the constant solicitation for an unnecessary surgery, Dean approached me and offered to help NOCIRC with our educational efforts. He began financing our booths at the national conventions of the American Academy of Pediatrics. We also ran an ad in *Parenting* magazine, reaching many parents. I was pleased with our outreach, but Dean told me that one day he intended to do "something big!"

Early in 2007, Dan Bollinger, then director of the International Coalition for Genital Integrity, organized a workshop with a San Francisco based strategy group called Smartmeme (now Center for

Story-Based Strategy) conducted by Patrick Reinsborough. Besides Dan, present were the directors and board members for the four major intactivist organizations at the time including John Geisheker and Dr. Mark Reiss for Doctors Opposing Circumcision, Steven Svoboda and Georganne Chapin for Attorneys for the Rights of the Child, and myself. Patrick had audited our websites and collateral for ideas, and we focused on developing unified messages for the movement. Little did we know at the time that this was the spark that would eventually lead to the founding of Intact America.

After a year, Dean said he wanted to be sure the money he was donating was well spent, and that he wanted to help the movement get to the next level of activism. Evidently, after 30 years a movement either grows to another level of success or it doesn't. I had begun my work 29 years earlier, so now was the time. I suggested a conference call with core activists—doctors, nurses, and lawyers who had been formulating strategies for the movement. Along with the movers and shakers, I invited Georganne Chapin, who had become increasingly involved with the movement, to join us on the call. Georganne was an attorney and an executive with experience running a large organization, and truly understood the harm of genital cutting. If anyone was qualified to carry our movement forward, I was sure it was Georganne.

As a result of this newfound coalition building, we met twice at Dean's office in Dallas with representatives from Aperio, a social-sector consulting firm Georganne found to help us move forward. We met with Warren Tranquada from Aperio for a third and final time in November 2007 at Georganne's Hudson Health Plan office in Tarrytown, New York. A business plan for a new non-profit organization was written and presented to us. They showed us the budget for the first year, one that required more money than I'd made in all the years I had been doing the work. Georganne was willing to head the organization, and Dan Bollinger proposed it be called Intact America.

Pleased with what we had done and confident in Georganne's abilities, Dean said he would contribute $1 million to our new organization. When I heard that, I burst into tears and just kept crying, relief flooding every cell of my body. Even as NOCIRC expanded, the movement grew, and I had more help, I was jubilant to have the worthiness of our movement confirmed and validated by both Dean, who was providing the means, and a team of activists who were committed to the work. We were moving forward toward the goals of educating parents, health professionals, and our culture—and protecting babies from unnecessary pain, trauma, and the many things that can go wrong with a surgical procedure on such a tiny, tender part of the body, as well as preserving the mother-child post-birth bond and ensuring a child's right to genital autonomy.

I now serve on the board of directors of Intact America, which is just as important to me as NOCIRC was in the beginning, and then Genital Autonomy-America. I am so proud and excited for the future that Intact America can promise beyond my years of service.

Chapter 28

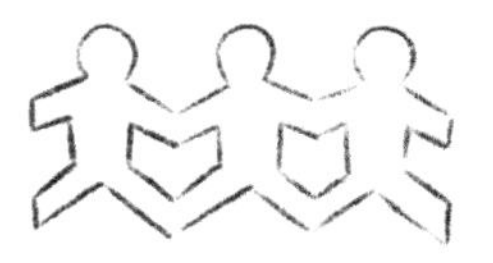

WHY ME?

As I finished up the work from my final symposium in 2018, wrote the 2019 *GA-America Annual Newsletter*, and began my work on this book, I noticed my vision was getting worse. The clouding of the lenses of my eyes was becoming more obvious, and I no longer felt safe driving at night. I called the ophthalmologist and had several appointments over the next few months.

In early 2020, I made an appointment with a local doctor for a required pre-surgical exam. However, the following week I received a call from my ophthalmologist, telling me that my surgery at Marin General Hospital (where I had been forced to resign 35 years earlier) was cancelled because, I was told, all *elective* surgeries had been cancelled due to the COVID-19 pandemic.

As soon as I hung up, I called Marin General Hospital to ask whether circumcisions, which are an *elective* surgery, had been cancelled due to the pandemic. I was told that they were still doing circumcisions. So, my elective surgery, which would help me see better and drive safely had been canceled, but a completely unnecessary elective surgery performed on tiny babies who could not consent—a surgery that would neither protect or enhance their health—was still being done? I was as incensed as the day I'd been told to keep my mouth shut about circumcision after recognizing that parents had a right to know the truth before signing their consent to the mutilation of their child. I didn't sleep for two nights as my brain worked through options about what to do next. Two days later, I sent this letter to Bradley P. Gilbert, Director of the California Department of Health Care Services, cc'ing Governor Gavin Newsom, two County Public Health officers, and the Division Director of Child Protective Services.

Re: Freeing up medical personnel and resources during COVID-19 pandemic emergency.

Dear Dr. Gilbert:

My cataract surgery at Marin General Hospital (MGH) in Marin County was cancelled recently because elective surgeries are not being done there at this time. So, I called MGH and asked if non-therapeutic neonatal circumcisions were also cancelled. I was told that circumcision is part of a "bundle package" for parents and they are still being performed at the hospital.

These elective, non-therapeutic surgeries use medical resources needed to fight the growing pandemic and they subject newborns to open wounds and infection. In the past few weeks, two newborn babies died from COVID-19—one in New Mexico and one in Connecticut. Circumcision can always be done but there is no way to bring back a dead baby. The U.S. Surgeon General and American College of Obstetrics and Gynecology warn against performing all elective surgeries. Doctors who are not complying with Federal and State recommendations must be reminded of their oath to "First, do no harm."

COVID-19 cases in Marin County are increasing. A moratorium on elective, non-therapeutic circumcision would free up resources as well as personnel to care for COVID-19 patients.

I hope you will help protect our most vulnerable citizens, COVID-19 patients and babies.

Sincerely,

Marilyn Fayre Milos, RN, Executive Director,

Genital Autonomy-America

None of them responded.

I decided not to have cataract surgery at Marin General Hospital when it became available again. I do not want to have my medical care at a facility where babies are circumcised. The health, safety, and well-being of its patients, especially when those patients are babies, is too impotant to me. Several weeks later, hospitals in California were rated by county. Marin General Hospital rated third in our county, which only has three hospitals. That cinched my resolve not to be a patient there and validated my experiences from the beginning of my quest for knowledge about circumcision that some administrators and personnel at MGH are ethically challenged.

Forty-one years after being forced to resign from Marin General Hospital, I learned that, after all my years of work with NOCIRC, other individuals, and organizations, after all the journal articles and medical books that have been published about short- and long-term harmful effects of circumcision, after the 15 International Symposia NOCIRC sponsored that gave doctors the opportunity to learn while accumulating continuing education credits, after all our demonstrations and protests, after the testimony of courageous men who have chronicled the harm done to them by circumcision, there seems to have been no observable change at this hospital. If we still need evidence to prove that appealing to those who profit from an uncaring or corrupt system is worthless, this provides us with an excellent example.

I cc'd Georganne on my letter and she said Intact America was going to do something, too. Intact America submitted a petition to the Surgeon General of the United States, addressing the pandemic and mentioning that elective circumcisions are still being done at hospitals during the pandemic, when non-therapeutic genital cutting dangerously violates a child's rights to security of person and bodily integrity. It was signed by people nationwide. The Surgeon General never responded.

Although we were disappointed with the reaction by government officials to the fact that healthcare providers continued to circumcise infants during the pandemic, we were, and remain, encouraged that growing numbers of parents are contacting our organizations and getting information from our websites.

In August 2020, however, something happened on the personal front of my family that was as troubling as the continuation of circumcisions during the pandemic. My oldest son Michael called to tell me he had cancer. Because of COVID-19, doctors had refused to see him earlier about the pain he was having in his lungs. He said, "Mom, I'm going to die from COVID, even though I've never had it, because doctors refused to see me for more than six months as my fast-growing cancer took over my body."

On a more serious scale than denying me my cataract surgery, doctors had denied my son the opportunity to live longer by deciding not to see him for symptoms that would have identified his lung cancer six months earlier. So, the medical establishment could take a beat from treating serious symptoms that resulted in death; but they could not pause in the delivery of routine unnecessary surgery on newborns. This was a new low point for me. *Was there any reason to trust doctors and hospital policies?*

On June 26, 2021, ten months after his diagnosis, Michael Paul Edmiston Preston died.

I am no stranger to loss, but nothing compares to the loss of a child. As sadness began to fill my heart with increasing darkness, I read something that changed my perspective. "Grief is love *persevering.*" The darkness I had felt was replaced with the light of loving memories. Now, when darkness lurks, I remember with gratitude the joy my son brought into my life.

Not long after that, my friend Patricia Acuña in Mexico sent these words that I shall never forget: "When our loved ones depart, they stop living among us to live within us." That was a reminder that the Universe is perfect as is.

Nine months after Michael's death, my daughter was diagnosed with bladder cancer. Kate didn't want to tell me because we'd just lost Michael, but I'm glad she did. Her first question to her doctor was, "Is this curable?" The doctor said it was and all her tests have shown the same thing. She had two masses removed from her bladder right away and then went through chemotherapy, which proved very trying for her. I hope and believe Kate will be the first person in our family to survive cancer. What a marvelous legacy for Kate... and a tremendous relief for her mother!

● ● ●

Before 1979, I wanted nothing more than to do the best I could in the field of nursing and to be a Certified Nurse Midwife, helping women and families have a joyful birth experience. When I received *NurseWeek* magazine's Nursing Excellence Award in May 2001, more than two decades after I began my work to end circumcision, it was for "outstanding advocacy for the past 22 years on behalf of those among us who are the most vulnerable and unable to protect themselves—infants and children," not for nursing or midwifery.

I've often wondered why it was *me* who took up the banner to end circumcision, as I was asked at dinner on the eve of the 2004 symposium in Padua, Italy. There were others who came before me who questioned or criticized circumcision and wrote articles about it. But for me, ending circumcision became my life's work. Investing over 40 years in understanding the origins of circumcision, the arguments surrounding it, and realizing the issue is more than medical—it is a violation of human rights—has been a natural process, one that paralleled my development and maturing as a daughter, mother, wife, partner, friend, student, nurse.

At the beginning, I did not realize I would become a target for ridicule, hostility, hatred, and venom. I even received death threats over the phone: "Milos, you're dead" and "We'll get you." No one ever took responsibility for the threats, and I was too angry to be scared for more than a minute. This misguided harassment impacted my life, but it didn't stop me. People might criticize me but they couldn't discredit me. I had the evidence.

This swirl of negative energy is a common response to new ideas that challenge our belief systems. Those familiar with hygiene protocols will know that in the 1870s Joseph Lister improved the chances for surviving surgery by using a spray of carbolic acid on wounds, dressings, and surgical tools, as well as by washing his hands before and after surgery. However, few remember Ignaz Semmelweis, the Hungarian physician who in 1847 first advanced the idea of "hand hygiene" in medical settings, after observing fewer maternal deaths when doctors washed their hands in between bare-handed examinations of diseased corpses and delivering babies.

Why wasn't Semmelweis credited with a revolutionary contribution to medicine? It was too soon and too radical for the medical establishment in Vienna. He was hounded and bullied and ended up in an asylum.

We think of medicine as a vitally progressive field in terms of innovations. Yet, it is undeniably slow to change when its conventions and methods are challenged, especially when there are financial incentives to stay the same.

Writing this memoir, I see more clearly how life prepared me for this calling. I was born to speak my truth, even if it resulted in one of my father's punches. My friends included people like Lenny Bruce, who taught me to keep calling out injustice, and to treat with equal dignity those on each side of the social divide, whether they are poor or rich.

Prior to my exposure to the pain and trauma of circumcision, I was part of an amazing cultural awakening, starting with the 1967 Summer of Love in San Francisco, followed by endless opportunities for clarifying my values and beliefs as the world and our country transformed into tangible local and global communities. A single mother with three children, I became involved with education reform, co-creating an alternative school and, after Matt and I moved our family to a more rural area in 1970, an alternative Open Classroom within a public school that is still operating today. I had a rich and varied training ground for shaping my activism.

Becoming involved with midwives and assisting with natural homebirths provided me with a network of alternative healthcare practitioners who fueled my desire to contribute to a beautiful birthing experience for every mother, father, and newborn. I was fiercely devoted to protecting the mother-infant bond. This led to my decision to become a Certified Nurse Midwife and my nursing school education. Then, once I witnessed a circumcision and heard the doctor say, **"There is no medical reason for doing this,"** there was no turning back from my call of duty to stop circumcision.

Why was it me who picked up the banner to crusade against the routine practice of circumcision? How could anyone witness a baby's reaction to genital cutting and not react to the excruciating physical pain and trauma the baby obviously was enduring?

Why me? I didn't have a choice. I could not turn away, could not close my eyes—and I certainly could not keep my mouth shut!

I recently asked a nursing-student colleague and long-time friend, Cynthia O'Keeffe, what she remembered about that first circumcision that we attended as students. Her perception was very much like mine and just as intense.

> *I think none of us was truly prepared for the ordeal we witnessed. The baby's cries, the pediatrician's comment that circumcision is medically unnecessary...and the poor infant, screaming until he checked out. You were the only one who took action to comfort the baby. I was transfixed with horror. I think I was truly afraid to move.The Clinical Group was silent and quite subdued during our debriefing, however, as we found our voices again, I think we found it both traumatic and completely irrational that anyone would voluntarily inflict so much pain and anguish on another, especially a newborn baby. The men, Michael, Eli, and Tony were quite upset; I remember Michael saying there was no way he would ever want that done to his child. I believe the majority of the group verbalized rejection of the surgery/mutilation.*

I know my reaction—I promised no child of mine would ever be subjected to circumcision, ever. As if the attack on a newborn's body isn't bad enough, my eyes and rational judgment told me the result of circumcision HAS to be deformity, dysfunction, and lasting emotional trauma. All newborn penises are tiny! How could a surgery on a small body part be anything but absolutely disastrous? Considering the size of a surgeon's hands, and the tiny, essential structures in a penis, I find it incredible that no doctor has condemned the practice due to extreme risk of hemorrhage and death.

On reflection, the most telling response of the poor baby was his unconsciousness after repeated screams of pain. His tears were still wet on his cheeks as his sobs became little double breaths. This, I thought, is the so called "sleep" described by doctors when they insist "the surgery causes minimal pain." Instead, what I saw was a response to excruciating pain. The mind cannot cope with physical damage and blocks the input by succumbing to an unconscious state. No wonder most babies cry when they are brought to the pediatrician's office! The conscious mind may forget, but the BODY remembers!

I appreciate Cynthia sharing her viewpoint, which validates my own. Maybe I was the only one who stepped forward to comfort the baby because I was the oldest student and a mother of three sons. I had never witnessed or understood this horrific surgical "procedure" to which my sons had been subjected based on the doctors' explanations and my husbands' consent. Maybe it was horror that led me to fight for the baby's right to an intact foreskin and against a purely cultural, non-medical, unethical practice to change nature's design. But it was love of these miraculous and perfect tiny human beings that sustained me.

It took stamina to withstand the reactions to my stance on circumcision during the early years, but I always knew I had right on my side. That didn't mean being rebuked, taunted, or losing friends didn't hurt, but it did *not* stop me. Nothing could have.

In addition, I have been blessed with a playful sense of humor that has allowed me to laugh my way through some of the most preposterous, crazy, illogical and irrational pronouncements you will ever encounter. Can you imagine not having a sense of humor when your life's passion is protecting newborn foreskins? I have fallen into the arms of friends and colleagues in fits of laughter as many times as I have collapsed from fatigue and a momentary feeling of failure. I could not have gotten through the last 40-plus years without laughing at myself (and others), and acknowledging the absurdity of many situations, while at the same time being driven to action by the gravity of the consequences of doing nothing.

Chapter 29

WHY YOU?

The repercussions of medically unnecessary routine infant circumcision and botched circumcisions are lifelong. The Circumcision Information and Resource Page online library includes a sad but eloquent testament to 65 babies and young people who have died from circumcision around the world since 1856, a small percentage of those we have lost.[75] A 2010 study published in the *Journal of Boyhood Studies* found that more than 100 neonatal circumcision-related deaths occur annually in the U.S.—all avoidable.[76] More recently, in Australia, where the rate of circumcision was about 80 percent in the 1950s, plunging to 20 percent today, a two-year-old boy died after a circumcision at a hospital in Western Australia, while his seven-month-old brother was in critical condition in an ICU after undergoing surgery to repair his botched circumcision.[77]

Several articles published in the *Palm Beach Post* in 2021 relay the story of a doctor in Palm Beach County, Florida, who botched two circumcisions—one resulting in amputation of the infant's penis in 2017, the other in the loss of a third of the infant's penis and the slicing of his urethra in February 2021.[78]

The physician, Dr. Berto Lopez, was responsible for 14 serious injuries to women and children, including 6 deaths, over his

33-year-career in Palm Beach County. He had been named in four disciplinary cases and nine malpractice actions. When an administrative law judge recommended a one-year suspension of Dr. Lopez's license, Elena Ris, Lopez's lawyer, said it was "extreme abuse of the system" for the board to revoke her client's license," and "This is not a man who is in any way a threat to society."[79]

Let that sink in. This is an example of the value our culture places on a physician's retention of his license over his responsibility for multiple deaths and disfigurement of women and babies. In 2021! Horrifying! Unacceptable!

Yet consider this. The United States Consumer Product Safety Commission reports recalls of toys and other products related to children all the time based on very few complaints. For instance, in April 2021, Battat recalled 61,000 Firefly Frank Infant Teethers after 14 reports of the wings detaching or pieces of the wing breaking off, including one report of a child choking on a broken piece of the wing.[80] In July 2021, Walgreen's recalled 54,000 Disney Baby Winnie the Pooh Rattle Sets due to eight complaints (and no injuries) because the feet on the rattle can detach, posing a choking hazard to young children.[81]

Why don't we have a consumer safety commission to protect infants, babies, and children from male genital mutilation, which obviously has serious risks? The U.S. Consumer Product Safety Commission, created to protect the public from unreasonable risks of injury or death associated with the use of thousands of types of products, has contributed to a decline in the rates of deaths and injuries due to poorly made consumer products over the past 40 years.

What am I missing? Why is it easier to recall thousands of toys that could be potentially hazardous to babies than it is to prevent one physician with a record of incompetence from mutilating women and babies? Where is the oversight when more than 100 deaths due to circumcision occur annually in the U.S., and who knows how many circumcisions are botched? We protect our children from even the remote possibility of injury or death from a toy, but not from an unnecessary medical surgery that can result in death or loss or mutilation of the male sex organ.

After all that has been uncovered and revealed about the risks versus benefits of circumcision, why is it still being offered by so many hospitals, often with inadequate information accompanying the consent form? On what basis is routine infant circumcision allowed when the U.S. Surgeon General has called for a suspension of all elective surgeries during a worldwide pandemic?

Intact America's 2020 Survey, a national, random sample of 2,519 mothers who had given birth to a boy in the past four years, provides insight into the reason for the high prevalence of circumcision in the U.S: solicitation by healthcare professionals. The survey defined "solicitation" as every time a physician, midwife, or nurse either verbally asked the mother if she wanted to circumcise her son; recommended she circumcise her son; told her that circumcision was required; handed her a circumcision consent form; or assumed (as perceived by the mother) that she wanted to circumcise her son.

Ninety-four percent of moms who gave birth to sons between 2017 and 2020 said they were asked, pressured, shamed, misled, or even coerced by doctors and nurses in healthcare settings to "consent" to the medically unnecessary, painful, and harmful removal of their baby boys' foreskins. The average number of solicitations was about eight, and some reported being asked more than a dozen times.

Results indicate that solicitation increased circumcisions by 173 percent. Intact America estimates that if circumcision solicitations were to cease, *600,000 boys a year* would be spared the trauma and risks of this unnecessary surgery.[82]

How do we challenge this paradigm?

First, the stakeholders must be stopped. Anyone who benefits financially from circumcision needs to be removed from the responsibility of informing parents about the risks and benefits of circumcision to a healthy intact baby. I've come to learn that this is not an easy task. People trust and believe their doctors and depend on them when they or their children need medical care. What parent wants to learn their doctor is willing to lie to them about the health benefits of circumcision and the trauma of the pain of surgery on one of the most sensitive parts of the human body? What parent wants to think that a professionally trained physician would unnecessarily amputate a normal part of their baby's body—and that the physician is paid extra for this, which muddies the waters of WHY?

Second, physicians and hospital administrators, as well as the medical companies that make the circumcision tools, need to be held directly accountable for their actions by consumers of healthcare. We need more monitoring of quality care and more feedback on its failures. This means the public, parents, and grandparents must speak up, using all forms of media, protest, and legal recourse. This is especially important for boys and men who have been directly affected by the consequences of circumcision, which takes a great deal of courage. Many refuse to acknowledge their PTSD from having their bodies and psyches forcibly and painfully altered without their consent. Those who do speak out still are at risk of having both the public and health community refuse to acknowledge their PTSD, and ridicule or laugh at them for telling the truth about their own painful and traumatic experience.

Third, nurses can be very effective, as members of the most hands-on healthcare delivery system in OB units, when they are educated and informed about the risks of circumcision and exchange information and concerns with each other. We know that many nurses courageously take a stand even when their jobs are on the line. I am still in awe of the Santa Fe nurses who became conscientious objectors in order to opt out of participating in circumcisions. It made a tremendous difference until St. Vincent Hospital was sold. In addition, as circumcision rates decline, nurses and nursing schools have an obligation to teach best practices regarding the care of intact male infants. I am counting on my sister nurses to take up the cause of ending circumcision and providing support for nature's gift of an intact penis.

Let's be honest. The average new parent in the United States does not understand that the majority of the world's males still have their foreskins—and experience none of the problems our doctors threaten will happen if our male babies are kept whole and normal. Nor do U.S. parents know that our country has higher rates of STIs, including HIV/AIDS, than other countries where the majority of males are intact. This makes no sense if, as some claim, circumcision "helps to prevent STIs."

Who does know this? Doctors who are educated, informed, and responsible. *Are there so few of them that it doesn't make a difference—or just too few willing to raise their voices? Or is the cultural norm of circumcision so rigid and powerful that these glaring inconsistencies make no difference?*

Yet, reading recent scientific studies and articles in my home, where I have spent the pandemic, I can say that the public and professional stance on circumcision is changing. There is now a demand for consistency in approaches to circumcision throughout the world. I know many physicians who support leaving baby boys' foreskins intact and have risked ridicule and censure to speak out on behalf of healthy infants. You will find some of their names in this book and in the Resources list at the end of it. I have the utmost respect and trust in the nurses who have walked this path with me and educated others to respect the intact body. The marvel and magic of technology puts the latest information at our fingertips, so we are never at a loss for data and stories that support the normal intact body and the end of circumcision.

All the medical excuses for circumcision have been debunked in medical and scientific studies. That leaves personal preference, cultural conditioning, religious affiliation, and financial incentive as reasons to justify amputating a normal body part from a non-consenting newborn baby or child. None of these excuses outweighs the right of a child to bodily integrity and genital autonomy. Genital cutting of non-consenting minor children, on its face, is just wrong. It is unethical and unlawful, too. So, how do we end it?

Many groups have formed to oppose circumcision since 1985 when Sheila Curran and I founded NOCIRC, the first national clearinghouse for information about circumcision. In its first decade it grew into an international network; 30 years later it had more than 110 centers worldwide. Although NOCIRC retired its name and adopted the name Genital Autonomy-America in January 2016, the website (nocirc.org) remains online as a valuable resource and much of the information has transferred to gaamerica.org. To facilitate distribution of knowledge, NOCIRC newsletters and pamphlets are not copyrighted. Others have created informative websites, too, so there is no excuse for anyone to live in the "dark ages" due to the lack of information that plagued me in 1958, 1961, and 1969 when my sons were born or in 1979 when I began my quest to educate myself about the reasons for and against circumcision.

In October 2021 GA-America merged with Intact America so that I could step back from running a non-profit organization after 36 years. On the Board of Directors for Intact America, and as a clinical consultant, I am still involved, but without the day-to-day responsibilities.

Intact America's founding goal is to change the way America thinks about circumcision. The organization not only keeps abreast of the latest research but commissions nationwide public surveys that have revealed changing public opinion regarding circumcision and the intact male body. A 2020 Intact America poll showed 21.5 percent alignment of the public with the statement that boys should be kept intact, up from only 1 in 10 in 2014.[83] Research has shown that 25 percent is the tipping point beyond which social change will make a shift.[84]

Intact America's position on circumcision is based on basic bioethical principles that include individual autonomy and informed consent; non-maleficence, that a medical practitioner "do no harm"; beneficence, the obligation to act for the benefit of the patient; and justice, equal treatment under the law to protect both boys and girls from non-consensual genital surgery/mutilation. These all should underlie good medical decisions regarding circumcision.[85] Intact America even has an "entry-level companion website" for learning the history of circumcision in America, plus a parent's guide for talking about it with doctors.

How do we end circumcision in the United States and grant the youngest members of our society autonomy over their own bodies? With your help!

The quickest way for individuals to become engaged in ending circumcision and promoting *every* child's right to an intact body is to join a group such as the ones mentioned in this book, which provide information, guidance, and support. But don't just educate yourself. The most important thing *you* can do to end circumcision is to start telling everyone you know about what you have learned.

Is "word of mouth" from someone new to this still-controversial arena really that important? Those who market any and everything know that consumers trust personal recommendations above all other sources of information in the buying process. According to a 2012 Nielsen poll, still quoted in 2022 as a gold standard, 92 percent of consumers *around the world* believe recommendations from friends and family over all forms of advertising.[86] So yes, *you,* speaking from the perspective of someone who has absorbed the available information about routine infant circumcision, or who has experienced regret from the decision to circumcise a child, or who has experienced trauma from circumcision, or who has decided not to circumcise a baby, you can make a difference.

My dear readers, it is important to direct our energies in ways that will keep the current momentum going and expand rather than drain our individual energy. Four decades have taught me that while outrage and anger may fuel my dedication to the cause of ending circumcision, and that promoting the natural body and protecting children seems to be in my DNA—that's not what changes things. Individuals arguing, pointing out inconsistencies between scientific facts and accepted theories, expecting rational fairness, justice, and compassion in the face of bureaucratic stagnation—these things make an impression, but they don't necessarily work. If the world were a rational place, retaining a baby's foreskin would never have been an issue.

My daughter Kate was 16 when I began my work and has always been supportive and helpful. She educated her friends about the benefits of leaving their babies intact, but just as important she discussed the meaning of that decision with her son, Matthew.

My grandson, born in 1982, had been doing outreach to educate people about circumcision since the age of five and, from the beginning, was a very articulate advocate for protecting babies. Before Matthew entered kindergarten, I talked to him about how children sometimes made fun of kids who were different from them, or the way they thought another child should look. I told him that children in my kindergarten class called me "four eyes" because I wore glasses, and that I was crushed by their hurtful name-calling. I said that because many boys in his class were circumcised they might tease him for being intact because his penis looked different. I was proud of both my grandson and my daughter Kate when five-year-old Matthew responded, "Don't worry, Nana, I won't tease them back. They've been hurt enough already!"

On his first day of school in the Open Classroom, the children sat in a circle and their teacher, Judy, introduced each of the children. When it came to Matthew's introduction, Judy said, "Matthew, when your mother was in my class, your grandmother used to come to school to teach anatomy to the children." Matthew replied, "Well, my Nana can't do that now because now she's stopping circumcision in America!"

When Matthew came home from school that day, he said, "Nana, I did a teaching at school today!" One of the mothers, a Jewish nurse with an intact son, told me what he had said, and that one of the children then asked, "What's circumcision?" Matthew, sounding like a five-year-old answered, "It's a yucky thing they do to babies."

When he was 18, I asked Matthew if he had ever been teased about being intact. He had been well-educated, having attended our meetings, demonstrations, and symposia, so I always hoped that had been enough to protect him. He replied, "Nana, everyone knows I am proud to be intact so no one would ever tease me. In my high school classes, though, I would mention the subject whenever I could. In psychology class, I mentioned how the pain and trauma of circumcision psychologically affect a baby. In history class, I said that circumcision was done to prevent masturbation because people thought that's what caused disease. In geography class, I told the class where male and female circumcision began and how it spread." I was happy to know he'd learned these things from his exposure to the issue. He went on to tell me, "So, in every class, students knew I was going to speak out. Some would roll their eyes and say, 'Here he goes again.' But, one day, they'll have babies, and they'll remember that one person in their class was willing to talk about it. Maybe I've helped protect their babies."

And that is exactly what happened. When two of his English teachers brought their babies to class to meet the students, Matthew asked, "Now, is he still as he was when he came into the world?"

Both teachers said, "Yes, Matthew, because of you."

That's how word of mouth works.

● ● ●

Even after circumcision ends, we will still have a nation of boys and men who suffered pain and trauma shortly after birth and continue to suffer today. We know that the pain and trauma of circumcision is carried in our bodies and psyches, individually and collectively. Those who recognize the lifelong consequences of genital cutting cannot take back our own pain or the pain we may innocently or unknowingly have caused our loved ones. But we do have the ability to bring about change that is transformative and, in that, we have healing and hope.

Albert Schweitzer said, "I don't know what your destiny will be, but one thing I know: the only ones among you who will be really happy are those who will have sought and found how to serve."

I have now done this work for more than half my life and I have felt blessed every step of the way. Starting out as just one person speaking out, I grew to know many who shared my concern. NOCIRC and the symposia were like a big tent where we would gather to exchange information and offer support and stories. Today I am proud and thankful to know there is a growing chorus around the world working to protect infants and children from unnecessary genital cutting of *all* children. It feels like we are one big family.

In March 2023, I had my 83rd birthday. I have become an old lady who has lived a fulfilling life of service and experienced the incandescent power of love of family, friends, strangers, humanity, and especially a love for babies and the mother/caregiver bond. I now find myself learning how to live in an aging body that is not always fully powered or firing on all cylinders, although my voice remains clear and loud, and I never tire of conversation and laughter.

I believe love, commitment, and encouraging an exchange of knowledge is the key to change. What works is speaking the truth. Please add your voice to that of others until we are heard.

My dream is for the day doctors no longer ask parents if they want their baby cut, parents no longer ask doctors to cut their babies, children no longer blame their parents, parents no longer need to ask forgiveness, and the whole sordid circumcision industry will no longer be a part of our human experience. Then, I believe, we will have a more peaceful world.

If Anything is Sacred
The Human Body is Sacred.
Walt Whitman
The Children of Adam

RESOURCES

BOOKS

Bodily Integrity and the Politics of Circumcision: Culture, Controversy, and Change. George C. Denniston, Frederick M. Hodges, and Marilyn Fayre Milos, eds. New York: Springer Publishing, 2006.

Born Both: An Intersex Life. Hida Viloria. New York: Hatchette Books, 2017.

Celebrating Brit Shalom. Lisa Brave Moss and Rebecca Wald. Oakland, CA: Notim Press, 2015.

Circumcision: A History of the World's Most Controversial Surgery. David Gollaher. New York: Basic Books, 2001.

Circumcision: An American Health Fallacy. Edward Wallerstein. New York: Springer Publishing Company, 1980.

Circumcision and Human Rights. George C. Denniston, Frederick M. Hodges, and Marilyn Fayre Milos, eds. New York: Springer Publishing, 2008.

Doctors Re-examine Circumcision. Thomas J. Ritter, MD, and George C. Denniston. Seattle: Third Millennium Publishing, 1992.

Flesh and Blood: Perspectives on the Problem of Circumcision in Contemporary Society. George C. Denniston, Frederick M. Hodges, and Marilyn Fayre Milos, eds. New York: Kluwer Academic/Plenum Press, 2004.

Genital Autonomy: Protecting Personal Choice. George C. Denniston, Frederick M. Hodges, and Marilyn Fayre Milos, eds. New York: Springer Publishing, 2010.

Genital Cutting: Protecting Children from Medical, Cultural, and Religious Infringements. George C. Denniston, Frederick M. Hodges, and Marilyn Fayre Milos, eds. New York: Springer Publishing, 2013.

The Girl with Three Legs: A Memoir. Soraya Miré. Chicago: Lawrence Hill Books. 2011.

The Joy of Uncircumcising! Restore Your Birthright and Maximize Sexual Pleasure. Jim Bigelow. Self-published: Hourglass Book Publishing, 1992.

Male and Female Circumcision: Medical, Legal, and Ethical Considerations in Pediatric Practice. George C. Denniston, Frederick M. Hodges, and Marilyn Fayre Milos, eds. New York: Kluwer Academic/Plenum Press, 1999.

Marked in Your Flesh: Circumcision from Ancient Judea to Modern America. Leonard B. Glick. Oxford, UK: Oxford University Press, 2005.

Prisoners of Ritual: An Odyssey into Female Genital Circumcision in Africa. Hanny Lightfoot-Klein. Oxfordshire, UK: Routledge, 1989.

Questioning Circumcision: A Jewish Perspective. Ronald Goldman. New York: Vanguard Press, 1998.

Sexual Mutilations: A Human Tragedy. George C. Denniston and Marilyn Fayre Milos, eds. New York, Plenum Publishers, 1997.

A Surgical Temptation: The Demonization of the Foreskin & the Rise of Circumcision in Britain. Robert Darby. Chicago: University of Chicago Press, 2005.

Understanding Circumcision: A Multi-Disciplinary Approach to a Multi-Dimensional Problem. George C. Denniston, Frederick M. Hodges, and Marilyn Fayre Milos, eds. New York: Kluwer Academic/Plenum Press, 2001.

What Your Doctor May Not Tell You About Circumcision: Untold Facts on America's Most Widely Performed— and Most Unnecessary—Surgery. Paul Fleiss. New York: Warner Books, 2002.

ARTICLES, ORGANIZATIONS, WEBSITES

Attorneys for the Rights of the Child, https://www.arclaw.org.

Beyond the Bris, https://www.beyondthebris.com.

Canadian Foreskin Awareness Project, http://www.can-fap.net./

Circumcision Harm Documentation Survey, http://circumcisionharm.org/results.htm.

Circumcision Information and Resource Pages, http://www.cirp.org/.

Doctors Opposing Circumcision, https://www.doctorsopposingcircumcision.org.

"Fine-Touch Pressure Thresholds in the Adult Penis." Morris L. Sorrells, James L. Snyder, Mark D. Reiss, Christopher Eden, Marilyn F. Milos, Norma Wilcox, Robert S. Van Howe, eds. *BJU International*, 19 March 2007, 99:864-69. https://doi.org/10.1111/j.1464-410X.2006.06685.x.

Genital Autonomy America, https://www.gaamerica.org.

Intact America, https://www.intactamerica.org.

Intact America has an excellent repository of videos on their YouTube channel, https://www.youtube.com/@IntactAmerica/videos.

NOCIRC, http://www.nocirc.org/.

Nurses for the Rights of the Child, Childrightsnurses.org.

ABOUT THE AUTHORS

Marilyn Fayre Milos

Born in San Mateo, California, and professionally trained as a Registered Nurse at the College of Marin's School of Nursing, Marilyn Fayre Milos began campaigning against elective non-therapeutic circumcision of male infants when, as a nursing student in 1979, she witnessed the circumcision of a newborn baby boy. Once she researched the issue and realized that most of the world's males are *not* circumcised, the important protective, immunological, and sexual functions of the foreskin, and the harmful consequences of inflicting pain and trauma on a newborn baby, she began giving parents accurate information about circumcision. Due to her commitment to informed consent, she was forced to resign from her position as a post-partum nurse at Marin General Hospital in 1985. Milos co-founded NOCIRC (National Organization of Circumcision Information Resources Center that same year. As executive director of NOCIRC, Milos coordinated 15 International Symposia on Genital Autonomy, emphasizing circumcision of infants and children as a human rights issue. NOCIRC's name was changed to Genital Autonomy-America in 2016 to reflect its mission to protect the bodily integrity of every child—female, male, and intersex. She is currently a member of the advisory board of Your Whole Baby and a member of the Board of Directors of Intact America.

After leaving the world of hands-on nursing in 1985, Milos was given the California Nurses' Association Award for Clinical Excellence in Perinatal Nursing in April 1988 for her dedication and unwavering commitment to righting a wrong. *NurseWeek* magazine honored Milos with its Nursing Excellence Award for Patient Advocacy in May 2001 and *Mothering Magazine* recognized Milos as "A Living Treasure" in its March 2008 issue. She received Intact America's Award for Humanitarian Service in 2009 and the Trustbirth Initiative Lifetime Achievement for Protecting Newborns in March 2010. In May 2015, Milos was honored as a "Living Legend" at the BirthKeeper Summit in Berkeley, California, for her work to end male, female, and intersex genital mutilation. Marilyn raised four children and has three grandchildren, and lives in Forest Knolls, Marin County, California.

Judy Kirkwood

Award-winning writer and editor Judy Kirkwood has worked on numerous book projects in a range of fields as a ghostwriter, cowriter, developmental and copy editor, and book doctor for over three decades. She is also the author of hundreds of lifestyle and health articles for dozens of publications and websites. Kirkwood was a major contributor to thirdage.com, a health and wellness site for women, and on the original Parent Advisory Board for Partnership for a Drug-Free America (now Partnership to End Addiction), drugfree.org. A resident of Delray Beach, Florida, Judy is the mother of two adult sons and grandmother to four girls.

ACKNOWLEDGMENTS

I have been privileged to live a life of service that I believe has made a difference in the development of young bodies, minds, and spirits. I am deeply grateful to everyone who has shared their wisdom and experiences with me, but I must thank several people in particular.

A special thank you goes to my daughter Kate Edmiston for understanding and helping me with my work from the very beginning; Sheila Curran, RN, who stood with me to support our important crusade; Dr. Dean Edell for championing our cause on his radio and television shows that gave us national attention; my son Troy Christian for contributing his artistic skills and creating our important educational videos.

Thanks to Ken Brierley, who had the courage to join me and provide his emotional support, his expertise with everything mechanical or technical, and his "blue collar" editorial suggestions. And to my stepdaughters Donelle and Crystal, who protected their sons.

Many wonderful friends and colleagues took time to offer their input and support as I was writing this book. Thank you, Meryn Callander and Pam Leo, who read an early draft and wondered why I hadn't included myself in the story. They insisted that I write about my journey along with that of the movement. I heard you and I did. Thanks, too, to my high school friend, English teacher and editor Marty Simmons, for her helpful suggestions; to George Hill for his eagle eye and content additions; and to Mary Conant; Jack Travis; and Sami A. Aldeeb Abu-Sahlieh, Doctor of Law and Staff Legal Advisor for the Swiss Institute of Comparative Law; and to Tina Kimmel.

I offer my deep appreciation to my Somali daughter Soraya Miré for taking the time to read earlier drafts, encouraging me to keep going, and offering help and advice. Both Soraya and Troy insisted I begin by describing the experience that changed my life.

To my three sons Michael, Troy, and Timothy, I wish had protected you, and appreciate beyond measure how you have valued my work. To Timothy and my daughter Kate, thank you for protecting my grandsons Demetri and Matthew, the latter who founded NOCIRC KIDS when he was 10 years old. Much appreciation also goes to my longtime friend Chelo Jacob and her son, my godson Jesse, who have supported my work for all these years.

I am gratified and pleased to pass the torch I have carried to Georganne Chapin, who has brought her organizational expertise to guiding Intact America into the future, with the goal of ending genital cutting in America. She has supported and helped me since we first met and continues to add to the legacy of the movement with her own book, *This Penis Business: A Memoir*. Georganne offered me important suggestions and encouragement as we shared the experience of writing our memoirs. She introduced me to my publisher Echo Garrett and to Judy Kirkwood, a brilliant editor who helped to finalize my manuscript and turn my story into an accurate and readable book. Thank you, Judy.

Marilyn Milos
Forest Knolls, California
July 2023

NOTES

CHAPTER 5

1. RoosaTikkanen, Munira Z. Gunja, Molly FitzGerald, Laurie Zephyrin, "Maternal Mortality and Maternity Care in the United States Compared to 10 Other Developed Countries." The Commonwealth Fund, Issue Brief, November 18, 2020. https://www.commonwealthfund.org/publications/issue-briefs/2020/nov/maternal-mortality-maternity-care-us-compared-10-countries.
2. Ibid.
3. Ibid.
4. Rabah Kamal, Julie Hudman, and Daniel McDermott, "What Do We Know About Infant Mortality in the U.S. and Comparable Countries?" Health System Tracker, October 18, 2019. https://www.healthsystemtracker.org/chart-collection/infant-mortality-u-s-compare-countries/#item-neonatal-mortality-is-highest-among-infants-of-black-mothers-.

CHAPTER 6

5. Edward Wallerstein, *Circumcision: An American Health Fallacy* (New York: Springer Pub Co, 1980), p. xviii. Sadly, this book is out of print. I suggest if you want a copy, you contact Springer Publishing via their website at http://www.springerpub.com. Maybe if they get enough requests, they will reprint it.
6. Ibid., p. 9.
7. Ibid., p. 217, Table B2.

8. Ibid., p. 4.
9. Ibid., p. 27.
10. Ibid., p. 32.
11. Historical Marker Data Base, https://www.hmdb.org/m.asp?m=106480.
12. Wallerstein, p. 67.
13. Ibid., p. 69.
14. Ibid., p. 70.
15. Ibid., pp. 12-13.
16. Ibid., p.86; note refers to Elizabeth Barrett-Connor, "Personal Prophylaxis for Venereal Disease," *Medical Aspects of Human Sexuality*, 12:5, May 1978, p. 154.
17. Ibid., p. 197.
18. Ibid., p. 192.

CHAPTER 7

19. Cory SerVaas, MD, "Health Groups Conclude Routine Circumcision Not Recommended." *Saturday Evening Post*, December 1981, pp. 26, 28, 29.
20. Carl Otten, MD, "The Case Against Newborn Circumcision." Ibid., p. 116.

CHAPTER 8

21. https://birthpsychology.com/apppahs-history/#.
22. https://birthpsychology.com/our-mission/.
23. Fran Porter and Dr. Richard Marshall et al., "Infants Feel Circumcision Pain, Study Says."

https://www.upi.com/Archives/1986/12/06/Researcher-says-newborns-register-pain/2099534229200/.

24. Ibid.
25. Paul S. Williamson, MD, FAAFP, and Marvel L. Williamson, RN, MSN, "Physiologic Stress Reduction by a Local Anesthetic During Newborn Circumcision." *Pediatrics* (71:36-40), 1983. http://www.cirp.org/library/pain/williamson/.

CHAPTER 9

26. William E. Schmidt, "A Circumcision Method Draws New Concerns." *New York Times,*October 8, 1985.

CHAPTER 10

27. Vincent Lupo, "Family Gets $2.75 Million in Wrongful Surgery Suit." *Lake Charles American Press*, Wednesday, May 28, 1986. http://www.cirp.org/news/1986.05.28_lawsuit/.
28. Edgar Schoen, "Ode to the Circumcised Male," *American Journal of Diseases of Children* (141:2), February 1987.
29. https://www.imdb.com/title/tt0672524/. There we are, listed in the cast, Marilyn Milos and Edgar Schoen.
30. Thomas Wiswell, "Corroborative Evidence for the Decreased Incidence of Urinary Tract Infections in Circumcised Male Infants." *Pediatrics* (78:1 July 1986). https://publications.aap.org/pediatrics/article-abstract/78/1/96/54158/Corroborative-Evidence-for-the-Decreased-Incidence?redirectedFrom=fulltext.
31. Thomas Wiswell, "The Age-Old Question of Circumcision." *Boston Globe*, June 22, 1987, p. 43.

32. L. Smith, R. Greenup, and E. T. Takafuji, "Circumcision as a Risk Factor for Urethritis in Racial Groups." *American Journal of Public Health* (77, 4: 452-4), April 1, 1987. https://doi.org/10.2105/AJPH.77.4.452.

CHAPTER 11

33. View the episode at https://www.youtube.com/watch?v=19E-qYM2oaQ.

34. Tom Shales, "Score One for Phil Donahue." *Washington Post*, November 6, 1987. https://www.washingtonpost.com/archive/lifestyle/1987/11/06/score-one-for-donahue/090e7901-0e70-45ac-8b68-2c9f56d09628/.

35. John M. Foley, MD, "The Unkindest Cut of All." *FACT* (3:4) July-August 1966. http://www.cirp.org/news/1966.07_Foley/.

36. Howard J. Stang, MD, et al., "Local Anesthesia for Neonatal Circumcision: Effects on Distress and Cortisol Response." *Journal of the American Medical Association* (259,10:1507-11), 1988. doi:10.1001/jama.1988.03720100025033.

CHAPTER 12

37. Maria Owings, Ph.D., Sayeedha Uddin, M.D., M.P.H., and Sonja Williams, M.P.H., Division of Health Care Statistics, "Trends in Circumcision for Male Newborns in U.S. Hospitals: 1979-2010." Center for Disease Control, August 2013, Table. https://www.cdc.gov/nchs/data/hestat/circumcision_2013/circumcision_2013.pdf.

38. See the Genital Autonomy America website for resources on the international symposia NOCIRC sponsored: https://www.gaamerica.org/international-symposia/.

CHAPTER 14

39. Benjamin Spock, MD, "Circumcision—It's Not Necessary." *Redbook,* April 1989. https://canadiancrc.com/Newspaper_Articles/Redbook_Dr_Benjamin_Spock_Against_Circumcision_April_1989.aspx.

CHAPTER 15

40. Mary Conant, interview with Cat Saunders that originally appeared in *The New Times*, February 1995 and is reprinted on the Nurses for the Rights of the Child website http://childrightsnurses.org/index.php/nurses-stories/nurses-speak-out-against-circumcision/.
41. Ibid.
42. Information about the history of the conscientious objectors of St. Vincent was compiled from several articles, including Betty Katz Sperlich, RN; Mary Conant, RN and Frederick Hodges, medical historian, "RN Conscientious Objectors to Infant Circumcision." *Revolution: The Journal of Nurse Empowerment*, March 1995, pp. 1-2. Angela Starks, "Nurses Just Say No." *SATYA* magazine, April 2005. http://www.satyamag.com/apr05/starks.html; reprinted on the Nurses for the Rights of the Child website: http://childrightsnurses.org/index.php/nurses-stories/nurses-just-say-no/. https://www.consciencelaws.org/background/policy/institutions-001.aspx. See my book, co-edited with George Denniston, *Sexual Mutilation: A Human Tragedy* (1997) for more on the St. Vincent Nurses actions.
43. Gussie Fauntleroy, "Infant Circumcision: The Debate Over Parents' Rights, Human Rights and the Right to Choose." *The New*

Mexican, Santa Fe, July 30, 2001: accessible at http://www.cirp.org/news/newmexican07-30-01/.

CHAPTER 16

44. Lisa Wendall, "Fighting to save boys pain: Marin woman leads anti-circumcision drive." *Marin Independent Journal*, May 21, 1983.

CHAPTER 18

45. https://docs.legis.wisconsin.gov/1995/related/acts/365.pdf.
46. View at https://www.youtube.com/watch?v=YeJlo9RmI-8.
47. https://consciouswoman.org/senator-dorothy-rupert/.
48. http://www.leginfo.ca.gov/pub/95-96/bill/asm/ab_2101-2150/ab_2125_bill_960923_chaptered.html.

CHAPTER 19

49. James DeMeo, "The Geography of Male and Female Genital Mutilation," George Denniston and Marilyn Fayre Milos, ed., *Sexual Mutilations: A Human Tragedy* (New York: Springer Publishing, 1997).
50. Ibid.
51. Douglas Gairdner, "The Fate of the Foreskin: A Study of Circumcision." *British Medical Journal* 2: 1433-1437, December 24, 1949. http://www.cirp.org/library/general/gairdner/.
52. See the complete text of Ashley Montague's Petition to the World Court here: http://www.nocirc.org/symposia/fourth/prescott.html.

CHAPTER 20

53. K.J. Anand and P.R. Hickey, "Pain and Its Effects in the Human Neonate and Fetus." *New England Journal of Medicine* (317: 1321-29). http://dx.doi.org/10.1056/NEJM198711193172105.

CHAPTER 21

54. American Academy of Pediatricians, Task Force on Circumcision, "Policy Statement on Circumcision." *Pediatrics* (103, 3: 686-93), March 1, 1999. http://www.cirp.org/library/statements/aap1999/.
55. Wallerstein, Appendix B, Table B-2
56. https://publications.aap.org/pediatrics/article/130/3/e756/30225/Male-Circumcision.
57. https://publications.aap.org/pediatrics/article-abstract/131/4/796/31907/Cultural-Bias-in-the-AAP-s-2012-Technical-Report?redirectedFrom=fulltext.
58. https://circumcision.org/circumcision-policies-of-international-organizations/.

CHAPTER 23

59. https://caselaw.findlaw.com/nd-supreme-court/1433915.html.
60. http://www.cirp.org/news/theforum07-09-03/.
61. http://www.cirp.org/news/theforum05-13-04/.
62. Information on the Sweet case was gathered from several sources: http://www.noharmm.org/sweet.htm; http://www.cirp.org/news/2000.03.08_Sweet/; http://www.touchngo.com/sp/html/sp-4188.htm; https://www.leagle.com/decision/19941185881p2d30411185.
63. https://www.bruchim.online/inclusion-directory/.

CHAPTER 24

64. Milton Diamond and H. Keith Sigmundson, "Sex Reassignments at Birth: A Long-Term View and Clinical Interpretations. *Archives of Pediatric and Adolescent Medicine* (151, 3: 298-304), March 1987. http://www.hawaii.edu/PCSS/biblio/articles/1961to1999/1997-sex-reassignment.html.
65. John Colapinto, "Gender Gap: What Were the Real Reasons Behind David Reimer's Suicide? *Slate*, June 3, 2004. https://slate.com/technology/2004/06/why-did-david-reimer-commit-suicide.html.
66. http://www.Intersexionfilm.com.
67. See https:/interactadvocates.org/, the website of Interact: Advocates for Intersex Youth.

CHAPTER 25

68. Australia's presentations were published in our book, George C. Denniston, Frederick Mansfield Hodges, and Marilyn Fayre Milos, eds., *Understanding Circumcision: A Multi-Disciplinary Approach to a Multi-Dimensional Problem* (New York: Springer, 2001).
69. DaiSik Kim, SA Koo, and Myung-Geol Pang, "Decline in Male Circumcision in South Korea." *BMC Public Health* 12: 1067 (2012). https://doi.org/10.1186/1471-2458-12-1067.
70. Morris L. Sorrells, James L. Snyder, Mark D. Reiss, Christopher Eden, Marilyn F. Milos, Norma Wilcox, Robert S. Van Howe. "Fine-Touch Pressure Thresholds in the Adult Penis." *BJU International* (99, 4:864-9), March 19, 2007.

CHAPTER 26

71. https://www.dw.com/en/german-regional-court-outlaws-child-circumcisions/a-16051790.

72. https://www.ncbi.nlm.nih.gov/pmc/articles/PMC6748459/.

73. https://www.bbc.com/news/magazine-18793842.

74. https://publications.aap.org/pediatrics/article/130/3/585/30235/Circumcision-Policy-Statement.

CHAPTER 29

75. Circumcision and Information Resource Page, http://www.cirp.org/library/death/.

76. Dan Bollinger, "Lost Boys: An Estimate of U.S. Circumcision-Related Infant Deaths." *Thymos Journal of Boyhood Studies* (4,1: 78-90), 2010. https://www.researchgate.net/publication/240804903_Lost_Boys_An_Estimate_of_US_Circumcision-Related_Infant_Deaths.

77. MarooshaMazafar, "Two-Year-Old Boy Dies and Baby Has Emergency Surgery After Botched Circumcision in Western Australia." *Independent*, December 9, 2021,https://www.independent.co.uk/news/world/australasia/perth-toddler-dies-botched-circumcision-b1972695.html.

78. Holly Baltz, "5 Takeaways: *Palm Beach Post* Investigation into Florida OB-GYN and Babies, Moms Who Died Under His Care." *Palm Beach Post*, September 23, 2021, https://www.palmbeachpost.com/story/news/2021/09/23/west-palm-ob-gyn-malpractice-lawsuits-moms-babies-died-circumcisions-botched-doctor-kept-practicing/5524867001/.

79. John Pacenti, "Florida Medical Board Vows to Address Red Tape Gap after Botched Circumcision," *Palm Beach Post*, June 5, 2021(updated September 17, 2021). https://www.palmbeachpost.com/story/news/2021/06/05/florida-medical-board-vows-address-red-tape-gap-after-botched-circumcision/7547826002/.
80. https://www.cpsc.gov/Recalls/2021/Battat-Recalls-Infant-Teethers-Due-to-Choking-Hazard-Sold-Exclusively-at-Target.
81. https://www.cpsc.gov/Recalls/2021/Walgreens-Recalls-Disney-Baby-Winnie-the-Pooh-Rattle-Sets-Due-to-Choking-Hazard.
82. https://intactamerica.org/press-release-having-a-baby-boy-get-ready-for-the-circumcision-sellers/.
83. https://intactamerica.org/kevin-nelson-a-long-time-advocate-for-children-and-a-noted-health-care-leader-joins-intact-americas-board-of-directors/.
84. Damon Centola, "The 25 Percent Tipping Point for Social Change." *Psychology Today*, May 29, 2019. https://www.psychologytoday.com/us/blog/how-behavior-spreads/201905/the-25-percent-tipping-point-social-change.
85. https://intactamerica.org/our-positions/.
86. https://www.buyapowa.com/blog/92-of-consumers-trust-word-of-mouth/; https://www.nielsen.com/us/en/insights/report/2012/global-trust-in-advertising-and-brand-messages-2/.

INDEX

D

N

Printed in the USA
CPSIA information can be obtained
at www.ICGtesting.com
LVHW011113150224
771930LV00013B/679

9 781950 495498